100 MENTAL MATHS

100
MENTAL
MATHS
ACTIVITIES

YEAR 1

**Ann Montague-Smith
and Margaret Gronow**

Authors
Ann Montague-Smith
Margaret Gronow

Illustrations
Louise Gardner

Series Designer
Sonja Bagley

Designer
Quadrum Solutions Ltd

Mixed Sources
Product group from well-managed
forests and other controlled sources
www.fsc.org Cert no. TT-COC-002769
© 1996 Forest Stewardship Council

Text © Ann Montague-Smith
and Margaret Gronow
© 2010 Scholastic Ltd

Designed using Adobe InDesign

Published by Scholastic Ltd
Book End
Range Road,
Witney
Oxfordshire OX29 0YD

www.scholastic.co.uk

Printed by Bell and Bain Ltd, Glasgow

1 2 3 4 5 6 7 8 9   0 1 2 3 4 5 6 7 8 9

British Library Cataloguing-in-Publication Data
A catalogue record for this book is available from the British Library.

ISBN 978-1407-11415-6

The rights of Ann Montague-Smith and Margaret Gronow to be identified as the authors of this work have been asserted by them in accordance with the Copyright, Designs and Patents Act 1988.

Extracts from the Primary National Strategy's *Primary Framework for Mathematics* (2006) www.standards.dfes.gov.uk/primaryframework © Crown copyright. Reproduced under the terms of the Click Use Licence.

Every effort has been made to trace copyright holders for the works reproduced in this book, and the publishers apologise for any inadvertent omissions.

CONTENTS

Introduction

About the series

100 Mental Maths Activities is a series of six photocopiable teachers' resource books, one for each of Years 1–6. Each book offers a bank of mental maths activities, each designed to last between five and ten minutes. The activities are designed to fit the planning guidelines of the *Renewed Framework for Teaching Mathematics* (2007) and are therefore divided into five Blocks with three Units of work in each Block.

This series provides a valuable accompaniment to *100 Maths Framework Lessons* (Scholastic, 2007). The mental maths activities are designed to accompany lessons in the framework series and grids are provided at the start of each Block to indicate the lesson and page numbers of the associated lesson plans in the relevant *100 Maths Framework Lessons* book. Used together, the teacher will have a rich bank of resources, activities and questions, offering greater choice and variety, while keeping to a closely similar mathematical content and progression. It is for the teacher to decide when to repeat an activity and when to move on: the exact mix of consolidation and progression needed will vary from one class to another. However, the series is also wholly appropriate for independent use alongside any maths scheme of work.

The six Rs of oral and mental work

In addition to matching the content of the Renewed Framework, this series also reflects the six features of children's mathematical learning that oral and mental work can support identified by the Primary National Strategy when renewing the Framework. The 'six Rs' provide a valuable guide to the purposes of each starter and a 'type of starter' is offered alongside each of the activities in this book.

The six types of starter include:

- rehearse: practicing and consolidating known skills

- recall: securing knowledge of facts – usually number facts

- refresh: drawing on, revisiting or assessing previous knowledge and skills

- refine: sharpening methods and procedures (eg mental strategies)

- read: using mathematical vocabulary and interpreting mathematical images, diagrams and vocabulary correctly

- reason: using and applying acquired knowledge and skills; using reasoning to draw conclusions.

For further information on the 'six Rs' visit the National Strategies website: *www.nationalstrategies.standards.dcsf.gov.uk.*

About the book

Each book provides support for teachers through 15 units of mental maths, developing and practising skills that will have been introduced, explained and explored in your main maths lesson time. Few resources are needed, and the questions for each activity are provided in full. The books are complete with answers, ready for you to pick up and use.

The activities are suitable for use with single- or mixed-ability groups and single- or mixed-age classes, as much emphasis has been placed on the use of differentiated and open-ended questions. Differentiated questions ensure that all the children can be included in each lesson and have the chance to succeed; suitable questions can be directed at chosen individuals, almost guaranteeing success and thus increased confidence.

Several essential photocopiable resource pages are also included (see pages 88–95). These resources are listed alongside each activity where required and should be prepared in advance of each mental maths session.

Each activity in this book has one or more learning objective based on the Year 1 teaching programme in the Renewed Framework. Curriculum grids are presented at the start of each Block to assist teachers with their planning and to highlight links with the related *100 Maths Framework Lessons* title. Alongside the activity description, required resources are highlighted, as well as the 'type of starter' (see above for further information). Where appropriate a 'mental strategy' for solving a number sentence or problem is suggested. Discussion of the children's methods is encouraged, since this will help the children to develop mathematical language skills: to appreciate that no single method is necessarily 'correct' and that a flexible repertoire of approaches is useful; to improve their overall confidence as they come to realise that all responses have value. Strategies are encouraged that will enable the children to progress from the known to the unknown number facts, thus developing their ability to select and use methods of mental calculation.

In Year 1, emphasis is placed on strategies for addition and subtraction (especially with numbers up to 30): adding from the larger number; partitioning; using doubles and 'near' doubles; counting up for a small difference. Repeated opportunities for counting in ones, twos, fives and tens will help to develop the children's understanding of patterns in times tables. Some lessons are based on telling the time and on using money. Games are included in each term's work to help provide variety and generate enthusiasm for numbers. Open-ended questions are used to challenge the children and extend their thinking.

The completion of the work in this book gives a sound basis for work in Year 2 and subsequent years, covered by the later books in the series. By following the lessons in this series of books, children will develop a variety of strategies for the solution of mathematical problems and will learn to be flexible in their approach to numerical work.

Transitional assessments

Transition is a time when, historically, children dip in their performance. Why this occurs is open to discussion but schools are increasingly aware of the need to accurately track children during these periods in order to ensure, as far as possible, a smooth learning journey. Transitional assessment is therefore important not just as a tool for summative judgements at the end of a school year, but also for communicating with teaching colleagues across the school.

100 Mental Maths Activities Year 1 includes two photocopiable single-level transitional assessments – both an oral and practical assessment and an oral and mental test – for levels 1 and 2, which will provide evidence of where children have reached in relation to national standards. Printable tests, mark schemes and answer sheets are available on pages 96-111.

BLOCK A

Unit 1

100 Mental Maths Starters				100 Maths Lessons		
Page	Objective	Activity title	Starter type	Unit	Lesson	Page
8	Count reliably at least 20 objects, recognising that when rearranged the number of objects stays the same.	(1) Counting cubes	Refresh	1	3	10
9	Compare and order numbers, using the related vocabulary.	(2) Number before, number after	Rehearse	1	4, 5	10, 11
10	Read and write numerals from 0 to 20, then beyond; use knowledge of place value to position these numbers on a number track and number line.	(3) Number 1-1 line build	Rehearse	1	6	12, 13
10	Say the number that is 1 more or less than any given number.	(4) 1 more or 1 less	Recall	1	7	13
11	Relate addition to counting on; recognise that addition can be done in any order; use practical and informal written methods to support the addition of a one-digit number or a multiple of 10 to a one-digit or two-digit number.	(5) Counting on to add	Refine	1	8	14
12	Understand subtraction as 'take away' and find a 'difference' by counting up; use practical and informal written methods to support the subtraction of a one-digit number from a one-digit or two-digit number and a multiple of 10 from a two-digit number.	(6) Take away	Refine	1	10	15

Unit 2

100 Mental Maths Starters				100 Maths Lessons		
Page	Objective	Activity title	Starter type	Unit	Lesson	Page
13	Count reliably at least 20 objects, recognising that when rearranged the number of objects stays the same; estimate a number of objects that can be checked by counting.	(7) Counting objects	Rehearse	2	1	23, 24
14	Compare and order numbers, using the related vocabulary.	(8) 1 more and 1 less	Recall	2	4	25, 26
14	Read and write numerals from 0 to 20, then beyond.	(9) Read numbers to 10	Recall	2	3	25

Unit 2 ...continued

	100 Mental Maths Starters				**100 Maths Lessons**		
Page	Objective	Activity title	Starter type	Unit	Lesson	Page
15	Relate addition to counting on; recognise that addition can be done in any order; use practical and informal written methods to support the addition of a one-digit number or a multiple of 10 to a one-digit or two-digit number.	⑩ Number 1–1 track adding	Refine	2	7	28, 29
15	Understand subtraction as 'take away' and find a 'difference' by counting up; use practical and informal written methods to support the subtraction of a one-digit number from a one-digit or two-digit number and a multiple of 10 from a two-digit number.	⑪ Taking away	Refine	2	9	30
16	Use the vocabulary related to addition and subtraction and symbols to describe and record addition and subtraction number sentences.	⑫ Subtraction facts	Read	2	10	30

Unit 3

	100 Mental Maths Starters				**100 Maths Lessons**		
Page	Objective	Activity title	Starter type	Unit	Lesson	Page
16	Compare and order numbers, using the related vocabulary.	⑬ Order numbers to 20	Refresh	3	1	37, 38
17	Read and write numerals from 0 to 20, then beyond; use knowledge of place value to position these numbers on a number track and number line.	⑭ Working with number lines	Read	3	3	38, 39
17	Say the number that is 1 more or less than any given number, and 10 more or less for multiples of 10.	⑮ 1 more or 1 less	Recall	3	5	40
18	Relate addition to counting on; recognise that addition can be done in any order; use practical and informal written methods to support the addition of a one-digit number or a multiple of 10 to a one-digit or two-digit number.	⑯ Add by counting on	Refine	3	8	42, 43
19	Understand subtraction as 'take away' and find a 'difference' by counting up; use practical and informal written methods to support the subtraction of a one-digit number from a one-digit or two-digit number and a multiple of 10 from a two-digit number.	⑰ Show me a difference	Refine	3	9	43
20	Use the vocabulary related to addition and subtraction and symbols to describe and record addition and subtraction number sentences.	⑱ Addition word problems	Refine	3	10	43

① **Counting cubes**

Resources Six cubes or other counting items per child	**Learning objective** Count reliably at least 20 objects, recognising that when rearranged the number of objects stays the same. **Type of starter** Refresh **Mental strategies** Ask the children to put their cubes in different positions and places. Help them to see that the number stays the same.
No set answers	Ask the children to count six cubes. Count together. Ask them to put the cubes in a straight line. *How many do you have?* Ask them to count from the other end. *How many do you have now?* Ask the children to do the following and count the cubes each time:

1. spread out their cubes on the table

2. make a tower

3. make a snake

4. hide them under their hands

5. put them in a circle

6. hide them under their hands, then close their eyes

7. walk round the room and count them when they get back

8. jump up and down four times, then count them again.

(2) # Number before, number after

Learning objective	Resources
Compare and order numbers, using the related vocabulary.	A class number line showing 1–10
Type of starter Rehearse	

Count together from 1 to 10. Count round the class from 1 to 10. Count backwards together from 10 to 1. Count round the class from 10 to 1.

No set answers

Ask individuals to touch numbers on the number line:

1. the number 4

2. the number that comes after 4

3. the number that comes before 4

4. the number 6

5. the number that comes after 6

6. any number bigger than 6

7. a number that is smaller than 6

8. the number 3

9. the number that comes after 3

10. a number that is smaller than 3

11. the number 9

12. the number that comes before 9

13. the number that is 1 more than 9

14. the number 5

15. the number that is 1 more than 5.

BLOCK A

③ **Number 1-1 line build**

Resources	Learning objective
Numeral cards 1–10 (enlarged from photocopiable page 88)	Read and write numerals from 0 to 20, then beyond; use knowledge of place value to position these numbers on a number track and number line.
	Type of starter Rehearse

No set answers

Give the cards 1–5 to a small group of children. Ask them to build a number line. *Is the number line right?* Count together forwards and backwards. Repeat using different children.

Then complete the number line to 10 and ask:

1. Which number comes after 4?
2. Which number comes after 7?
3. Which number comes before 3?
4. Which number comes before 9?
5. Tell me a number that is bigger than 2.
6. Tell me a number that is bigger than 5.

④ **1 more or 1 less**

Resources	Learning objective
Number track 1–10 (enlarged from photocopiable page 90)	Say the number that is 1 more or less than any given number.
	Type of starter Recall
	Mental strategies Suggest that the children 'see' a mental number line in their heads to help them to find the number 1 more/less. If children struggle, provide copies from the resource sheet Number tracks 1–10.

No set answers

Ask the children to count together from 1 to 10, then back again. Now ask them to count until you say *Stop. What was the last number you said? What will the next number be? What is the number before…?*

Repeat this several times, stopping on different numbers. Keep the numbers small at first then extend to up to 10. For example:

1. 3
2. 2
3. 5
4. 1
5. 7

⑤ **Counting on to add**

Learning objective
Relate addition to counting on; recognise that addition can be done in any order; use practical and informal written methods to support the addition of a one-digit number or a multiple of 10 to a one-digit or two-digit number.

Type of starter
Refine

Mental strategies
Emphasise that the last number in the count is the number of objects altogether.

Resources
Two PE hoops; a selection of objects (for example blocks, yoghurt pots, large fir cones); numeral cards 1–5 (enlarged from photocopiable page 88)

Ask one child to put three objects into one hoop. Ask another child to put two objects into the other hoop. Ask: *How many are there altogether?* All count 3 and 2 together, then count 2 and 3 together. Show the card for 5. Continue with:

1. 2 and 1

2. 1 and 3

3. 4 and 0

4. 3 and 1

5. 2 and 2

6. 1 and 4

7. 5 and 0

8. 1 and 1

9. 4 and 1

10. 2 and 3

Answers
1. 3
2. 4
3. 4
4. 4
5. 4
6. 5
7. 5
8. 2
9. 5
10. 5

BLOCK A

⑥ **Take away**

Resources	Learning objective
One PE hoop; a selection of objects (eg bricks, yoghurt pots, large fir cones)	Understand subtraction as 'take away' and find a 'difference' by counting up; use practical and informal written methods to support the subtraction of a one-digit number from a one-digit or two-digit number and a multiple of 10 from a two-digit number.

Type of starter
Refine

Answers

1. 2
2. 2
3. 1
4. 4
5. 0
6. 3
7. 0
8. 4
9. 1
10. 0
11. 2
12. 3
13. 2
14. 2
15. 1

Ask a child to put four objects into the hoop. Ask another child or the children to check that there are four objects. Ask another child to take away one object. *How many are left?* Count together.

Encourage the children to give a subtraction sentence. All say together: '4 take away 1 is 3.'

Repeat this sequence for each question.

1. 3 take away 1
2. 4 take away 2
3. 2 take away 1
4. 5 take away 1
5. 2 take away 2
6. 5 take away 2
7. 3 take away 3
8. 4 take away 0
9. 2 take away 1
10. 5 take away 5
11. 5 take away 3
12. 4 take away 1
13. 2 take away 0
14. 4 take away 2
15. 3 take away 2

⑦ Counting objects

Learning objective
Count reliably at least 20 objects, recognising that when rearranged the number of objects stays the same; estimate a number of objects that can be checked by counting.

Type of starter
Rehearse

Resources
Nine cubes for each child

Ask the questions in sequence. Children should raise a hand to answer.

1. Count out nine cubes.

2. Take one away. How many now?

3. Take away another four. How many do you have now?

4. Add two cubes. Count the cubes.

5. Add another three cubes. How many now?

6. Take seven away. How many are left?

7. Take two away. How many do you have?

8. Add eight cubes. Count the cubes.

9. Take away three. How many do you have?

10. Add four. How many do you have now?

Answers

1. 9
2. 8
3. 4
4. 6
5. 9
6. 2
7. 0
8. 8
9. 5
10. 9

BLOCK A

(8) **1 more and 1 less**

Resources
Numeral cards 0-10 (enlarged from photocopiable page 88) for each child

Learning objective
Compare and order numbers, using the related vocabulary.

Type of starter
Recall

Mental strategies
Children may need to count up to the number in their heads. Then they either count on one (1 more) or back one (1 less).

No set answers

Ask the children to spread out their numeral cards in front of them, in number order. Explain that you will say a number. Then you will ask them to hold up the numeral card that is 1 more than this number. Repeat this for 1 less than the number given. When the children are confident, ask for either 1 more or 1 less so that they have to listen carefully to the instruction.

To begin with, use the numbers 1 to 6, then extend to up to 10. For example:

1.	3	4.	6
2.	5	5.	8
3.	2		

(9) **Read numbers to 10**

Resources
A board or flipchart; numeral cards 0-10 (enlarged from photocopiable page 88) for each child

Learning objective
Read and write numerals from 0 to 20, then beyond.

Type of starter
Recall

Answers
1. 8
2. 9
3. 7
4. 3
5. 6
6. 8
7. 7
8. 6
9. 5
10. 8

Ask the children to put their cards in order on the table.

Ask them to hold up the card with the answer. Choose an individual to write each answer on the board.

Show me:

1.	8	6.	the number 2 more than 6
2.	the number 1 more than 8	7.	7
3.	the number 1 less than 8	8.	the number 1 less than 7
4.	3	9.	the number 1 more than 4
5.	the number 6	10.	the number 1 less than 9

⑩ Number 1-1 track adding

Learning objective	Resources
Relate addition to counting on; recognise that addition can be done in any order; use practical and informal written methods to support the addition of a one-digit number or a multiple of 10 to a one-digit or two-digit number.	A number track 1–10 (from photocopiable page 90) for each child

Type of starter Refine

Ask the children to put a finger on the number 2. Tell them: *We are going to count on 3 with a finger from the other hand.* The children say: '1, 2, 3.' Ask: *What number have you landed on?* Say together: *2 add 3 equals 5.*

1.   Start on 1, count on 4

2.   Start on 2, count on 1

3.   Start on 5, count on 2

4.   Start on 1, count on 3

5.   Start on 3, count on 3

6.   Start on 2, count on 6

7.   Start on 5, count on 3

8.   Start on 4, count on 1

9.   Start on 1, count on 5

10.   Start on 5, count on 1

After the last two questions, ask: *Which was easier?* Ask the children to explain.

11.   Start on 1, count on 7

12.   Start on 7, count on 1

13.   Start on 3, count on 6

14.   Start on 6, count on 3

Conclude that it is easier to count on from the larger number.

Answers

1.   5
2.   3
3.   7
4.   4
5.   6
6.   8
7.   8
8.   5
9.   6
10.   6
11.   8
12.   8
13.   9
14.   9

⑪ Taking away

Learning objective	Resources
Understand subtraction as 'take away' and find a 'difference' by counting up; use practical and informal written methods to support the subtraction of a one-digit number from a one-digit or two-digit number and a multiple of 10 from a two-digit number.	Five cubes for each child

Type of starter Refine

Mental strategies
Encourage the children to count accurately what is left, then to say the subtraction sentence with you.

Ask the children to put their five cubes in front of them. Now say: *Take away 2 cubes. How many are left? Let's say the number sentence together. Five take away 2 leaves 3.* Repeat for other quantities to take away. Repeat for a different start number, such as 4.

1.   Take away 2

2.   Take away 4

3.   Take away 3

4.   Take away 1

5.   Take away 5

6.   Take away 0

Answers

1.   3
2.   1
3.   2
4.   4
5.   0
6.   5

BLOCK A

(12) Subtraction facts

Resources
Fact cards: subtraction (enlarged from photocopiable page 91); numeral cards 0–5 for each child (enlarged from photocopiable page 88)

Learning objective
Use the vocabulary related to addition and subtraction and symbols to describe and record addition and subtraction number sentences.

Type of starter
Read

Mental strategies
If children do not 'know' the answer, encourage them to count up from the smaller to the larger number, keeping a tally with their fingers. For example, for 5 – 3 they count: '3 and 4, 5. So the answer is 2.'

No set answers

Explain that you will hold up a subtraction fact card. Ask the children to work out the answer mentally. Then, when you say *Show me* they hold up the numeral card that is the answer. Check which children can answer with confidence and which children are not sure yet.

Unit 3

(13) Order numbers to 20

Resources
A washing line (or string), pegs, numeral cards 1–20 (enlarged from photocopiable pages 88 and 89)

Learning objective
Compare and order numbers, using the related vocabulary.

Type of starter
Refresh

No set answers

Explain that one end of the line represents 1 and the other end is 10.

Shuffle the cards 1–10 and place them face down. Ask a child to pick a card and peg it on the line in a sensible position. Do the other children agree with its position? Discuss this. Repeat for the other cards. When the line is complete, count along it in both directions together.

Repeat the game or progress to cards 11–20, explaining that one end of the line represents 11 and the other end is 20.

(14) # Working with number lines

Learning objective	Resources
Read and write numerals from 0 to 20, then beyond; use knowledge of place value to position these numbers on a number track and number line.	A class number line; numeral cards 1–10 (enlarged from photocopiable page 88)
Type of starter Read	

Start by counting together from 1 to 10. Repeat. Count together from 10 to 1. Repeat.

Deal out the numeral cards 1–10 to ten children.

Say: *Come here, number 2.* Ask the children to build a number line, working in both directions from 2. Ask: *Is their number line correct?* Count together forwards and backwards.

Repeat with different children, starting with:

1.   5   4.   9

2.   8   5.   4

3.   6   6.   3

No set answers

(15) # 1 more or 1 less

Learning objective	Resources
Say the number that is 1 more or less than any given number, and 10 more or less for multiples of 10.	Flipchart; numeral cards 0–20 for each child (enlarged from photocopiable pages 88 and 89)
Type of starter Recall	
Mental strategies Ask the children to explain how they worked out their answer.	

Provide each child with numeral cards 0–20. Explain that you will write a number, up to 10 at first, on the flipchart. Ask the children to find the 1 more and 1 less numbers on their cards. Say, for example:

1.   What is 1 more than 6?   4.   What is 1 less than 4?

2.   What is 1 less than 6?   5.   What is 1 more than 7?

3.   What is 1 more than 4?   6.   What is 1 less than 7?

Extend to numbers in the range 11–20.

7.   What is 1 less than 15?   10.   What is 1 less than 12?

8.   What is 1 more than 15?   11.   What is 1 more than 16?

9.   What is 1 more than 12?   12.   What is 1 less than 16?

Answers
1.   7
2.   5
3.   5
4.   3
5.   8
6.   6
7.   14
8.   16
9.   13
10.   11
11.   17
12.   15

(16) **Add by counting on**

Resources
Numeral cards 1–5 for each child (enlarged from photocopiable page 88)

Learning objective
Relate addition to counting on; recognise that addition can be done in any order; use practical and informal written methods to support the addition of a one-digit number or a multiple of 10 to a one-digit or two-digit number.

Answers

1. 4
2. 7
3. 5
4. 5
5. 7
6. 3
7. 6
8. 6
9. 4
10. 3

Ask the children to put their cards in order.

Count forwards and backwards. Encourage the children to touch each card as they say the number.

Say two numbers. The children move the cards with those numbers towards themselves and put a finger on the larger number. When you say *Show me,* they hold it up.

Ask the children to use their cards to find the answers to these addition sentences.

1. 3 and 1
2. 2 and 5
3. 1 and 4
4. 3 and 2
5. 4 and 3
6. 1 and 2
7. 4 and 2
8. 1 and 5
9. 1 and 3
10. 1 and 2

BLOCK A

 Show me a difference

Learning objective
Understand subtraction as 'take away' and find a 'difference' by counting up; use practical and informal written methods to support the subtraction of a one-digit number from a one-digit or two-digit number and a multiple of 10 from a two-digit number.

Type of starter
Refine

Mental strategies
Children should use the strategy of counting up from the smaller to the larger number, in ones. If children struggle, provide a 0–20 number line on which to count on. Ask: *How did you work that out?*

Resources
Individual whiteboards and pens

Explain that you will ask difference questions. Remind the children that they should count up from the smaller to the larger number. If necessary, work through an example together, such as: *What is the difference between 12 and 7?*

Now read out the following questions, asking the children to write their answers on their whiteboards. When you say *Show me* they must hold up their whiteboards.

1. What is the difference between 11 and 4?

2. How much more is 13 than 9?

3. What is the difference between 18 and 15?

4. Paul has 16 marbles. Peter has 12 marbles. Who has more? How many more?

5. Sara buys 14 apples. Tammy buys 9 apples. Who has fewer? How many fewer?

Answers
1. 7
2. 4
3. 3
4. Paul, 4
5. Tammy, 5

(18) **Addition word problems**

Resources
None

Learning objective
Use the vocabulary related to addition and subtraction and symbols to describe and record addition and subtraction number sentences.

Type of starter
Refine

Mental strategies
Ask the children to explain how they solved each problem. They may count on in ones, use doubles or near doubles, or 'know' the answer.

Answers
1. 13
2. 6
3. 18
4. 12
5. 20

Explain that you will ask some addition word problems. Ask the children to work out the answers mentally then to put up their hands when they have the answer. Here are some examples. These problems can be adapted with different numbers if necessary.

1. Pippa has 7 badges. Tania has 6. How many do they have in total?

2. Fay has 14 beads. She needs 20 beads to make a bracelet. How many more beads does she need?

3. There are 12 cats and 6 dogs at the vets. How many animals is that in total?

4. A hen lays 6 eggs in a week. How many eggs will she lay in 2 weeks?

5. Fifteen cows live in a field. The farmer puts another 5 cows into the field. How many cows are there in total?

BLOCK B

Unit 1

	100 Mental Maths Starters				100 Maths Lessons		
Page	Objective	Activity title	Starter type	Unit	Lesson	Page
23	Solve problems involving counting, adding, subtracting, doubling or halving in the context of numbers, measures or money, for example to 'pay' and 'give change'.	⑲ Using coins	Refresh	1	3	57
24	Count reliably at least 20 objects, recognising that when rearranged the number of objects stays the same; estimate a number of objects that can be checked by counting.	⑳ Counting out	Rehearse	1	6	59, 60
25	Read and write numerals from 0 to 20, then beyond.	㉑ Reading and writing numbers	Read	1	7	60
26	Say the number that is 1 more or less than any given number, and 10 more or less for multiples of 10.	㉒ Show me (1 more or less)	Recall	1	8	61
27	Derive and recall all pairs of numbers with a total of 10 and addition facts for totals to at least 5.	㉓ Finger addition	Refine	1	11	64
28	Derive and recall all pairs of numbers with a total of 10 and addition facts for totals to at least 5.	㉔ Numeral 1–1 card addition	Recall	1	11	64
28	Derive and recall all pairs of numbers with a total of 10 and addition facts for totals to at least 5.	㉕ Number 1–1 line addition	Refine	1	11	64

Unit 2

	100 Mental Maths Starters				100 Maths Lessons		
Page	Objective	Activity title	Starter type	Unit	Lesson	Page
29	Visualise and name common 2D shapes and 3D solids and describe their features.	㉖ Name this shape	Recall	1	13,14	65
29	Visualise and name common 2D shapes and 3D solids and describe their features.	㉗ 2D shape sort	Recall	2	2	72, 73
30	Say the number that is 1 more or less than any given number, and 10 more or less for multiples of 10.	㉘ 10 more, 10 less	Refresh	2	4	73
31	Say the number that is 1 more or less than any given number, and 10 more or less for multiples of 10.	㉙ On or back in ones or tens	Recall	2	5	74

Unit 2 ...continued

	100 Mental Maths Starters			**100 Maths Lessons**		
Page	**Objective**	**Activity title**	**Starter type**	**Unit**	**Lesson**	**Page**
32	Recall the doubles of all numbers to at least 10.	㉚ 1 to 5 doubles	Rehearse	2	7	75
32	Derive and recall all pairs of numbers with a total of 10 and addition facts for totals to at least 5; work out the corresponding subtraction facts.	㉛ Show me (add and subtract)	Recall	2	8, 9	76, 77
33	Derive and recall all pairs of numbers with a total of 10 and addition facts for totals to at least 5.	㉜ Pairs to make 10	Refine	2	10	77
33	Derive and recall all pairs of numbers with a total of 10 and addition facts for totals to at least 5.	㉝ Cards to make 10	Recall	2	11	78, 79
34	Solve problems involving counting, adding, subtracting, doubling or halving in the context of numbers, measures or money, for example to 'pay' and 'give change'.	㉞ Buying and giving change	Rehearse	2	14	80

Unit 3

	100 Mental Maths Starters			**100 Maths Lessons**		
Page	**Objective**	**Activity title**	**Starter type**	**Unit**	**Lesson**	**Page**
35	Relate addition to counting on; recognise that addition can be done in any order; use practical and informal written methods to support the addition of a one-digit number or a multiple of 10 to a one-digit or two-digit number.	㉟ Counting 1-1 on addition	Refine	3	2	88, 89
35	Derive and recall all pairs of numbers with a total of 10 and addition facts for totals to at least 5.	㊱ Clock 10	Recall	3	2	88, 89
36	Recall the doubles of all numbers to at least 10.	㊲ Double it	Recall	3	3	89
36	Derive and recall all pairs of numbers with a total of 10 and addition facts for totals to at least 5.	㊳ Subtraction fact cards	Recall	3	5	91
37	Relate addition to counting on; recognise that addition can be done in any order; use practical and informal written methods to support the addition of a one-digit number or a multiple of 10 to a one-digit or two-digit number.	㊴ Larger number first	Refine	3	6	92
37	Understand subtraction as 'take away' and find a 'difference' by counting up; use practical and informal written methods to support the subtraction of a one-digit number from a one-digit or two-digit number and a multiple of 10 from a two-digit number.	㊵ Subtraction terminology	Refresh	3	8	93
38	Use the vocabulary related to addition and subtraction and symbols to describe and record addition and subtraction number sentences.	㊶ Word problems	Read	3	9	94
38	Visualise and name common 2D shapes and 3D solids and describe their features; use them to make patterns, pictures and models.	㊷ Make a shape pattern	Recall	3	12	96

(19) Using coins

Learning objective
Solve problems involving counting, adding, subtracting, doubling or halving in the context of numbers, measures or money, for example to 'pay' and 'give change'.

Type of starter
Refresh

Mental strategies
Encourage the children to visualise the coins mentally and to describe them. If they are unsure, ask them to look closely at the coins and describe colours and images.

Resources
Pot of coins for each group: 1p, 2p, 5p, 10p, 20p, 50p, £1, £2

Ask the children to listen to your instructions and to find a coin that fits the description. They should hold up their hands to show their chosen coin, then answer the related question.

1. Find the smallest silver coin. How much is it worth?

2. Find the coin worth the least. What colour is it? What is its name?

3. Find the coin that is worth more than £1. Which coin is it? What colour is it?

4. Find the coin that is worth between 1p and 5p. How much is it worth?

5. Find all the silver coins. Put them in order in front of you. Which one is worth least/most? How much is each one worth?

Now ask the children to use the coins to answer these questions.

6. A ball costs 18p. Which coins would you choose to pay for it?

7. A bag of toffees costs £3. How would you pay for it?

8. Choose the least number of coins to make 4p.

9. Jill spends 6p. Which coins could she use?

10. I have two £2 coins. How much money is that?

Answers
1. 5p
2. Bronze, 1p
3. £2, gold and silver
4. 2p
5. 5p, 10p, 20p, 50p. Least: 5p; most: 50p
6. 10p, 5p, 2p, 1p
7. £2 and £1
8. 2p and 2p
9. 5p and 1p; or three 2p coins; or six 1p coins
10. £4

BLOCK B

(20) **Counting out**

Resources	**Learning objective**
Twelve cubes for each child	Count reliably at least 20 objects, recognising that when rearranged the number of objects stays the same; estimate a number of objects that can be checked by counting.
	Type of starter
	Rehearse

Answers

3. 11
5. 10
6. 8
7. 12
8. 8
9. 12
10. 9

Ask the children to raise a hand to answer each question.

1. Make a line with your cubes. Count them.

2. Make two rows of six. Count the cubes.

3. Hold one cube in a hand. How many are on the table now?

4. Make a circle with all your cubes. Count them.

5. Put one cube in each hand. How many are on the table now?

6. Move four cubes away from the others. How many are left?

7. Put four cubes in a row, then two more rows of four. How many cubes are there altogether?

8. Take five cubes away. How many are left?

9. Put three cubes in a row, then three more rows of three. How many cubes are there altogether?

10. Take three cubes away. How many are left?

(21) Reading and writing numbers

Learning objective	**Resources**
Read and write numerals from 0 to 20, then beyond.	Individual whiteboards and pens; a board or flipchart

Type of starter
Read

Mental strategies
Encourage the children to 'see' the number in their heads so that they are using their mental image of it.

Explain to the children that you will say a number. Ask them to draw the number in the air, making large arm movements. Repeat this several times.

Ask them to write the number that you say onto their whiteboards. When you say *Show me* they must hold up their boards for you to see. Check that the numerals are written correctly. Where there are reversals make a note to discuss this with the children very soon.

Use the numbers 0–10. When the children are confident with these, extend, over time, to 20 and beyond.

Say, for example:

1.   Write the number 5.

2.   Write a number which has some curves.

3.   Write a number which is made of just straight lines.

4.   Write the number that comes between 2 and 4.

5.   Write the number that comes just after 6.

Where more than one answer is possible, for example questions 2 and 3, write the answers onto the flipchart. Ask the children to read these numbers aloud as you point to them.

Answers

2.   2, 3, 5, 6, 8, 9, 0

3.   1, 4, 7

4.   3

5.   7

BLOCK B

(22) **Show me (1 more or less)**

Resources
Numeral cards 0–10 for each pair (enlarged from photocopiable page 88)

Learning objective
Say the number that is 1 more or less than any given number, and 10 more or less for multiples of 10.

Type of starter
Recall

Mental strategies
Ask how the children worked out the answer. Encourage them to 'see' a mental number line on which they can count on or back.

No set answers

Ask the children to work in pairs.

They place one set of numeral cards 0–10 in order in front of them.

Explain that you will say a number. Ask them to work together to put out the number that you said, then the number that is 1 less and the number that is 1 more than the number that you said.

Repeat this several times.

Now ask the children to put the cards away. Explain that when you say a number you would like them to say three numbers in number order: the number 1 less, the number, then the number 1 more.

Keep the numbers within the range 1–10.

As children become more confident with this, extend to numbers more than 10.

(23) **Finger addition**

Learning objective Derive and recall all pairs of numbers with a total of 10 and addition facts for totals to at least 5. **Type of starter** Refine	**Resources** None

Explain that when you say a number, you want the children to hold up that number of fingers on one hand. (If necessary, demonstrate touching and raising one finger at a time from a folded hand.)

Show me...

1. three fingers

2. four fingers

3. five fingers

4. two fingers

5. zero (or nought) fingers.

Tell the children that they should now show the first number with one hand and the second number with the other hand.

Show me...

6. three fingers and one finger

7. five and two

8. one and four

9. two and zero (or nought)

10. three and five.

Explain that you are going to ask them: *How many fingers altogether?* They should use both hands to help them answer.

11. Two and one

12. Three and two

13. One and five

14. Four and three

15. Five and zero

Answers

11. 3

12. 5

13. 6

14. 7

15. 5

BLOCK B

(24) Numeral 1-1 card addition

Resources	**Learning objective**
Numeral cards 2-8 (enlarged from photocopiable page 88)	Derive and recall all pairs of numbers with a total of 10 and addition facts for totals to at least 5.
	Type of starter
	Recall

Answers

1. 3
2. 5
3. 2
4. 6
5. 4

6. 7
7. 3
8. 6
9. 8
10. 5

The children sit in a circle with the numeral cards spread out on the carpet. Ask them to add 1 in their heads to the number that you say (for example, 4). Ask an individual to hold up the relevant numeral card. Together say: '4 add 1 makes 5.'

Repeat for:

1.	2	4.	5
2.	4	5.	3
3.	1		

Ask the children to add 2 to the number that you say. Encourage them to hold the number in their heads and add 2 mentally.

6.	5	9.	6
7.	1	10.	3
8.	4		

(25) Number 1-1 line addition

Resources	**Learning objective**
A class number line	Derive and recall all pairs of numbers with a total of 10 and addition facts for totals to at least 5.
	Type of starter
	Refine

Answers

1. 3
2. 5
3. 4
4. 4
5. 5
6. 3
7. 2
8. 5
9. 2
10. 5

Ask the children to add together two numbers that you say. They can use the fingers on each hand for the two numbers.

Ask individuals to say and point to the number on the line. Each time, say the whole statement together (for example, '3 add 1 makes 4').

1.	2 add 1	6.	3 add 0
2.	4 add 1	7.	1 add 1
3.	1 add 3	8.	5 add 0
4.	2 add 2	9.	2 add 0
5.	1 add 4	10.	3 add 2

BLOCK B

 26 # Name this shape

Learning objective	**Resources**
Visualise and name common 2D shapes and 3D solids and describe their features.	3D shape models of a cube, cuboid, sphere, cylinder, pyramid and cone

Type of starter
Recall

Mental strategies
Encourage the children to recall the shape, and to see it in their minds.

Explain that you will hold up a shape. Ask the children to name the shape. Now ask them to explain how they know that this is the shape that they name. Repeat this for each shape.

Now ask them to find all the shapes that have:

1. just flat faces
2. a curved face
3. a square face
4. a rectangular face
5. no curved faces
6. a triangular face
7. a circular face

Answers

1. cube, cuboid, pyramid
2. sphere, cone, cylinder
3. cube, cuboid with square end faces
4. cuboid
5. cube, cuboid, pyramid
6. pyramid
7. cone, cylinder

 27 # 2D shape sort

Learning objective	**Resources**
Visualise and name common 2D shapes and 3D solids and describe their features.	2D shape tiles for squares, triangles, rectangles and circles for each group

Type of starter Recall

Mental strategies
Encourage the children to listen carefully. Check that they understand and sort appropriately. If you repeat this activity without the children sorting the shapes, they will build a mental image of the shape.

Explain that you will describe a flat shape. Ask the children to listen carefully and then pick up the shape that they think you are describing. They can sort the shapes, putting to one side the ones that do not fit your description after each sentence. Say, for example:

1. My shape has straight sides. All the sides are the same length. My shape has four sides.

2. My shape has one side. It is curved.

3. My shape has four sides. The sides are all straight. The opposite sides are the same length. Two sides are longer than the other two.

4. My shape has straight sides. It has three sides.

Answers

1. square
2. circle
3. rectangle
4. triangle

BLOCK B

(28) 10 more, 10 less

Resources
A tens number line 0–100 (from photocopiable page 92) for each child

Learning objective
Say the number that is 1 more or less than any given number, and 10 more or less for multiples of 10.

Type of starter
Refresh

Answers

1. 30
2. 70
3. 20
4. 80
5. 100
6. 30
7. 70
8. 20
9. 90
10. 40

Count together in tens from 0 to 100 and back again, with the children pointing to each number as it is said. Children should raise a hand to answer each question.

Say: *What comes … … on our line?*

1. after 20
2. after 60
3. after 10
4. after 70
5. after 90
6. before 40
7. before 80
8. before 30
9. before 100
10. before 50

(29) On or back in ones or tens

	Resources
Learning objective Say the number that is 1 more or less than any given number, and 10 more or less for multiples of 10. **Type of starter** Recall **Mental strategies** Encourage the children to count on or back in ones. Similarly, encourage the children to count on or back in tens. Ask them to shut their eyes and imagine a number line marked in ones or tens and to use this to help them to count on or back.	None

Explain that you will ask a '1 more or less' question. Invite the children to say the answer together on your signal.

1.   What is 1 more than 12?

2.   What is 1 less than 15?

3.   What is 1 more than 19?

4.   What is 1 less than 20?

5.   What is 1 more than 16?

Repeat this for 10 more and 10 less.

6.   What is 10 more than 20?

7.   What is 10 less than 50?

8.   What is 10 more than 80?

9.   What is 10 less than 100?

10. What is 10 less than 10?

Answers

1.   13
2.   14
3.   20
4.   19
5.   17

6.   30
7.   40
8.   90
9.   90
10. 0

(30) 1 to 5 doubles

Resources	**Learning objective**
A set of 'Domino doubles' cards (enlarged from photocopiable page 93)	Recall the doubles of all numbers to at least 10.
	Type of starter
	Rehearse

Answers

1. 4
2. 8
3. 6
4. 0
5. 10
6. 2

Shuffle the cards and place them face down on the carpet. Hold up one card. Ask the children what they can see ('both sides are the same', 'there are three dots and three dots', 'there are six dots' and so on). Discuss their answers and use the word 'double'.

Ask a child to choose a card and hold it up. Say together, for example: '3 add 3 makes 6. Double 3 makes 6.' Repeat with the other dominoes.

Finish by asking these questions. The children could use their fingers to show the answers.

1.	double 2	4.	double 0
2.	double 4	5.	double 5
3.	double 3	6.	double 1

(31) Show me (add and subtract)

Resources	**Learning objective**
None	Derive and recall all pairs of numbers with a total of 10 and addition facts for totals to at least 5; work out the corresponding subtraction facts.
	Type of starter
	Recall

Answers

1. 4
2. 4
3. 5
4. 5
5. 5
6. 2
7. 3
8. 5
9. 4
10. 1
11. 4
12. 1
13. 5
14. 0
15. 2
16. 2

Ask the children to show the answers on their fingers. Encourage recall of the number facts.

1.	2 + 2	9.	5 - 1
2.	3 + 1	10.	3 - 2
3.	1 + 4	11.	4 - 0
4.	5 + 0	12.	2 - 1
5.	2 + 3	13.	5 - 0
6.	1 + 1	14.	1 - 1
7.	2 + 1	15.	3 - 1
8.	3 + 2	16.	2 - 0

(32) Pairs to make 10

Learning objective Derive and recall all pairs of numbers with a total of 10 and addition facts for totals to at least 5.	**Resources** A number track 1–10 (from photocopiable page 90) for each child
Type of starter Refine	
Mental strategies Encourage the children to touch the number and count the 'steps' to 10.	

Ask: *How many do we need to add to 7 to make 10?* Count on together from 7. Children should raise their hands to answer.

1. 6
2. 3
3. 8
4. 5
5. 2

6. 1
7. 7
8. 10
9. 0
10. 4

Answers

1. 4
2. 7
3. 2
4. 5
5. 8
6. 9
7. 3
8. 0
9. 10
10. 6

(33) Cards to make 10

Learning objective Derive and recall all pairs of numbers with a total of 10 and addition facts for totals to at least 5.	**Resources** Four or more sets of numeral cards 1–9 (enlarged from photocopiable page 88)
Type of starter Recall	

Give each child one numeral card. More able children could have an extra card.

Explain that you want to know how many more to 10. The children with the correct card should hold it up and say the number.

Hold up your '6' card and say: *6 add how many equals 10?* The children with a '4' card should hold it up. Say: *6 add 4 equals 10.* Repeat this number fact together.

1. 8 + how many = 10?
2. 5 + how many = 10?
3. 9 + how many = 10?
4. 3 + how many = 10?
5. 4 + how many = 10?

6. 2 + how many = 10?
7. 7 + how many = 10?
8. 1 + how many = 10?
9. 6 + how many = 10?
10. 0 + how many = 10?

Answers

1. 2
2. 5
3. 1
4. 7
5. 6
6. 8
7. 3
8. 9
9. 4
10. 10

BLOCK B

 Buying and giving change

Resources
Pot of coins for each group: 1p, 2p, 5p, 10p

Learning objective
Solve problems involving counting, adding, subtracting, doubling or halving in the context of numbers, measures or money, for example to 'pay' and 'give change'.

Type of starter
Rehearse

Mental strategies
Ask the children to explain how they worked out each part of the answer. At this point ask the children to model the answers using coins.

Answers
1. 2p, 2p, 1p
2. 4p
3. 3 toffees; 1p change
4. 2p; 2p coin
5. 7p; 3p change; 2p and 1p or three 1p coins

Give each group a pot of coins. Explain that you will say some money problems. Ask the children to work mentally. However, if they are unsure they can use the coins to help them.

1. Stevie paid 5p for an orange. He used three coins to pay. Which three coins did he use?

2. Sophie bought some biscuits for 6p. How much change did she get from 10p?

3. Toffees cost 3p each. How many can I buy with a 10p coin? What change will I get?

4. I spend 8p on a pencil. How much change will I get from 10p? The shopkeeper gives me one coin for my change. Which coin do I get?

5. Sally buys a pear for 4p and an apple for 3p. How much does she spend? What change does she get from 10p? Which coins could the shopkeeper give her?

■SCHOLASTIC

(35) Counting 1-1 on addition

Learning objective
Relate addition to counting on; recognise that addition can be done in any order; use practical and informal written methods to support the addition of a one-digit number or a multiple of 10 to a one-digit or two-digit number.

Type of starter
Refine

Mental strategies
Remind the children that when adding, it is easier to count on from the larger number. Ask: *Which is the larger number, 4 or 2?* The children put a finger on 4 and count on 2. Say together: '4 add 2 equals 6.'

Resources
A number track 1-10 (from photocopiable page 90) for each child

Each time, ask: *Which is the larger number?* Encourage the children to put a finger on this number and count on from it with the other hand. They should raise a hand to give the answer.

1. 3 and 5	6. 4 and 1
2. 6 and 2	7. 5 and 2
3. 1 and 3	8. 5 and 1
4. 2 and 4	9. 2 and 6
5. 3 and 6	10. 2 and 3

Answers
1. 8
2. 8
3. 4
4. 6
5. 9
6. 5
7. 7
8. 6
9. 8
10. 5

(36) Clock 10

Learning objective
Derive and recall all pairs of numbers with a total of 10 and addition facts for totals to at least 5.

Type of starter
Recall

Resources
A board or flipchart

Draw a clock face as shown.

Ask the children to find the other number that can be added to each number on the clock face to make 10.
Ask volunteers to write each answer beside its 'partner' (see example in diagram).

When the diagram is complete, ask the children to go round the clock and say each addition sentence (for example, '3 add 7 makes 10').

No set answers

BLOCK B

(37) **Double it**

Resources A set of 'Domino doubles' cards (enlarged from photocopiable page 93)	**Learning objective** Recall the doubles of all numbers to at least 10. **Type of starter** Recall
No set answers	Explain that you will be asking the children to double numbers. Remind them that 2 + 2 = double 2 = 4. Ask a child to pick a domino card from the set (such as double 3) and hold it up for everyone to see. Ask for a volunteer to say what this double makes: 'Double 3 is 6.' Repeat this together. Repeat with a different child, until all the cards have been used at least twice.

(38) **Subtraction fact cards**

Resources A set of 'Fact cards: subtraction' (enlarged from photocopiable page 91)	**Learning objective** Derive and recall all pairs of numbers with a total of 10 and addition facts for totals to at least 5. **Type of starter** Recall
No set answers	Tell the children that you will hold up a subtraction card for them to read aloud with you. You will then ask for someone to give the answer. If the others agree, they should give it the 'thumbs up'; if not, they should give it the 'thumbs down'. Keep the pace as fast as possible. Make a note of how long it takes to work through all the cards. Repeat at a later date.

(39) Larger number first

Learning objective Relate addition to counting on; recognise that addition can be done in any order; use practical and informal written methods to support the addition of a one-digit number or a multiple of 10 to a one-digit or two-digit number. **Type of starter** Refine	**Resources** A number snake 0–20 (from photocopiable page 94) for each child

Ask the children to add two numbers by putting a finger on the larger number and counting on by the smaller number. They should wait to answer together when you say: *Now*.

1.	4 and 8	6.	2 and 5
2.	10 and 7	7.	3 and 1
3.	1 and 3	8.	10 and 4
4.	5 and 13	9.	8 and 6
5.	6 and 11	10.	6 and 12

Answers
1. 12
2. 17
3. 4
4. 18
5. 17
6. 7
7. 4
8. 14
9. 14
10. 18

(40) Subtraction terminology

Learning objective Understand subtraction as 'take away' and find a 'difference' by counting up; use practical and informal written methods to support the subtraction of a one-digit number from a one-digit or two-digit number and a multiple of 10 from a two-digit number. **Type of starter** Refresh **Mental strategies** For each question ask: *How did you work that out?* Discuss the strategies used. If necessary, model the question and work orally to show how to count up.	**Resources** None

Ask the children to work mentally. Remind them that they can count up from the lower number, keeping a tally with their fingers, to find the answer.

1. What is 17 take away 9?
2. What is the difference between 14 and 8?
3. How much more is 19 than 16?
4. What is the difference between 20 and 11?
5. What is 15 subtract 5?

Answers
1. 12
2. 6
3. 3
4. 9
5. 10

BLOCK B

(41) Word problems

Resources
Individual whiteboards and pens; flipchart

Learning objective
Use the vocabulary related to addition and subtraction and symbols to describe and record addition and subtraction number sentences.

Type of starter
Read

Mental strategies
Discuss with the children which strategies they used for each problem. Discuss combining, for example: 11 + 8 = 10 + 1 + 5 + 3 = 15 + 4 = 19.

Answers

1. 11 + 8 = 19; 19p
2. 20 - 16 = 4; 4p
3. 14 + 9 = 23
4. 18 - 8 = 10
    or 8 + 10 = 18
5. 18 - 11 = 7

Explain that you will pose an addition or subtraction word problem. Ask the children to work mentally to find the answer. They must write their answer as an addition or subtraction sentence on their whiteboards. When you say *Show me* they hold up their boards. It may be helpful to write the symbols for +, - and = on the flipchart as a reminder.

1. I buy an orange for 11p and a banana for 8p. How much do I spend?
2. I buy a book for 16p. How much change do I get from 20p?
3. Sue has 14 beads and Sally has 9 beads. How many beads is that altogether?
4. What is the difference between 18 and 8?
5. Eighteen birds sit on a wall. Eleven birds fly away. How many are left on the wall?

(42) Make a shape pattern

Resources
Either some 2D shape tiles (circles, squares, rectangles, triangles) or computer software that generates shapes

Learning objective
Visualise and name common 2D shapes and 3D solids and describe their features; use them to make patterns, pictures and models.

Type of starter
Recall

Mental strategies
Ask the children to explain how they know what comes next in the pattern, using shape names appropriately.

No set answers

Explain that you will begin a pattern: square, circle, square, circle... Ask the children to say what shapes are used, to say the pattern, and to say which shape comes next.

1. square, circle, square, circle
2. triangle, triangle, rectangle, triangle, triangle, rectangle
3. circle, square, triangle, circle, square, triangle
4. circle, circle, rectangle, rectangle, circle, circle, rectangle
5. square, triangle, circle, rectangle, square, triangle, circle, rectangle

BLOCK C

Unit 1

100 Mental Maths Starters				100 Maths Lessons		
Page	Objective	Activity title	Starter type	Unit	Lesson	Page
41	Answer a question by recording information in lists and tables.	㊸ Favourite colours	Read	1	2	104, 105
42	Answer a question by recording information in lists and tables; present outcomes using practical resources, pictures, block graphs or pictograms.	㊹ Wider and narrower	Read	1	3	105
43	Use diagrams to sort objects into groups according to a given criterion; suggest a different criterion for grouping the same objects.	㊺ Sorting shape tiles	Reason	1	1	103, 104
44	Estimate, measure, weigh and compare objects, choosing and using suitable uniform non-standard or standard units and measuring instruments (eg a lever balance, metre stick or measuring jug).	㊻ Longer and shorter	Rehearse	1	4, 5	106
45	Estimate, measure, weigh and compare objects, choosing and using suitable uniform non-standard or standard units and measuring instruments (eg a lever balance, metre stick or measuring jug).	㊼ Heavier and lighter	Rehearse	1	7	108
45	Estimate, measure, weigh and compare objects, choosing and using suitable uniform non-standard or standard units and measuring instruments (eg a lever balance, metre stick or measuring jug).	㊽ Comparing capacities	Rehearse	1	9	109, 110

Unit 2

100 Mental Maths Starters				100 Maths Lessons		
Page	Objective	Activity title	Starter type	Unit	Lesson	Page
46	Answer a question by recording information in lists and tables.	㊾ Car colours	Read	2	1	115, 116
47	Use diagrams to sort objects into groups according to a given criterion; suggest a different criterion for grouping the same objects.	㊿ Number sort	Reason	2	2	116

100 MENTAL MATHS ACTIVITIES · YEAR 1   39

Unit 2 ...continued

	100 Mental Maths Starters				100 Maths Lessons		
Page	Objective	Activity title	Starter type	Unit	Lesson	Page	
48	Answer a question by recording information in lists and tables; present outcomes using practical resources, pictures, block graphs or pictograms.	51 Pictogram	Read	2	4	117	
49	Use diagrams to sort objects into groups according to a given criterion; suggest a different criterion for grouping the same objects.	52 Sorting criteria	Reason	2	5	117	
50	Estimate, measure, weigh and compare objects, choosing and using suitable uniform non-standard or standard units and measuring instruments (eg a lever balance, metre stick or measuring jug).	53 Paper lengths	Rehearse	2	6	118, 119	
51	Estimate, measure, weigh and compare objects, choosing and using suitable uniform non-standard or standard units and measuring instruments (eg a lever balance, metre stick or measuring jug).	54 Using non-standard units	Recall	2	8	119, 120	

Unit 3

	100 Mental Maths Starters				100 Maths Lessons		
Page	Objective	Activity title	Starter type	Unit	Lesson	Page	
52	Answer a question by recording information in lists and tables.	55 Zoo animals	Read	3	1	125, 126	
53	Answer a question by recording information in lists and tables; present outcomes using practical resources, pictures, block graphs or pictograms.	56 Our pets	Read	3	2	126, 127	
53	Estimate, measure, weigh and compare objects, choosing and using suitable uniform non-standard or standard units and measuring instruments (eg a lever balance, metre stick or measuring jug).	57 Estimate and check	Rehearse	3	4	128, 129	
54	Estimate, measure, weigh and compare objects, choosing and using suitable uniform non-standard or standard units and measuring instruments (eg a lever balance, metre stick or measuring jug).	58 Box measuring	Rehearse	3	7, 8	130, 131	
55	Use diagrams to sort objects into groups according to a given criterion.	59 Counting pattern sort	Reason	3	9	131, 132	
56	Use diagrams to sort objects into groups according to a given criterion.	60 Shape sort	Reason	3	10	132	

(43) **Favourite colours**

Learning objective
Answer a question by recording information in lists and tables.

Type of starter
Read

Mental strategies
The children will need to read the colour names. If they find this difficult put a blob of the colour next to its name. They will need to order the numbers to find more/less popular colours.

Resources
A flipchart sheet with the 'Favourite colours' table below

No set answers

Favourite colours	
Blue	
Red	
Green	
Yellow	
Purple	

Explain to the children that you want to find out their favourite colours. Reveal the flipchart. Ask the children to put up their hands when you say their favourite colour. For each colour, count how many hands go up and write this number into the chart. Now ask:

1.   How many people liked red?

2.   How many people liked blue?

3.   Which was more popular, blue or red?

4.   Which colour was most popular?

5.   Which colour was least popular?

6.   Which colour was more popular than...? How can you tell?

7.   Which colour was less popular than...? How can you tell?

BLOCK C

(44) **Wider and narrower**

Resources
A flipchart with the 'Wider/Narrower' table below; strips of coloured paper, in pairs, of different widths and different colours; sticky-tack

Learning objective
Answer a question by recording information in lists and tables; present outcomes using practical resources, pictures, block graphs or pictograms.

Type of starter
Read

Mental strategies
Children may need help understanding that it is each pair of strips that is compared. Emphasise the fact that because a strip is in the wider column it does not mean that it will always be the wider strip. It may be narrower when compared with another strip.

No set answers

Wider	Narrower

Reveal the table. Now show the children the first pair of paper strips. Ask a child to compare the two for width. Ask: *Which is wider? Which is narrower?* Stick the strips into the appropriate columns. Repeat for another pair of strips until the table is complete. Pointing to different pairs ask:

1. Which is wider? How can you tell that?

2. Which is narrower? How do you know?

Now ask:

3. Which column on the table shows the narrower strips?

4. Which column on the table shows the wider strips?

(45) **Sorting shape tiles**

Learning objective
Use diagrams to sort objects into groups according to a given criterion; suggest a different criterion for grouping the same objects.

Type of starter
Reason

Mental strategies
Children need to recognise the properties of the shape tiles. If they are unsure, let them feel the sides of the shapes to recognise straight and curved.

Resources
A hoop; 2D shape tiles for sorting (squares, rectangles, circles, triangles)

Explain that you would like some help to sort some shape tiles according to your rules. Say, for example: *Put the shapes with straight sides in the hoop.*

1. Which shapes are in the hoop?

2. Which shapes are not in the hoop?

Say: *Now let's sort a different way. Put all the shapes that have four straight sides in the hoop.*

3. Which shapes are in the hoop?

4. Which shapes are not in the hoop?

Ask: *How else could we sort the shapes?*

Answers

1. squares, rectangles, triangles

2. circles

3. squares, rectangles

4. triangles, circles

46 Longer and shorter

Resources
A collection of objects that can be compared for length, such as pencils, rulers, books, ribbons and scarves; two hoops; labels 'Longer' and 'Shorter'

Learning objective
Estimate, measure, weigh and compare objects, choosing and using suitable uniform non-standard or standard units and measuring instruments (eg a lever balance, metre stick or measuring jug).

Type of starter
Rehearse

Mental strategies
Children will need to understand that when comparing items for length the items must be lined up to make a direct comparison.

No set answers

Put the two hoops with their labels on the floor so that all the children can see them. Now show them a ribbon. Ask them to help sort the other items by length, putting those longer than the ribbon into the 'Longer' hoop and those shorter than the ribbon into the 'Shorter' hoop. When the sorting is done ask:

1. Which items are longer than the ribbon?

2. Which items are shorter than the ribbon?

Now remove all the items from the hoops, choose another thing to compare, such as a ruler, and repeat the activity.

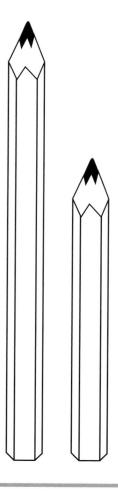

BLOCK C

47 Heavier and lighter

Learning objective Estimate, measure, weigh and compare objects, choosing and using suitable uniform non-standard or standard units and measuring instruments (eg a lever balance, metre stick or measuring jug). **Type of starter** Rehearse **Mental strategies** Children may confuse size with weight. Encourage them to feel the weights in their hands to decide which is heavier.	**Resources** Items to compare by holding, such as small parcels of different weights and sizes; a bucket balance

Explain that you want to compare how heavy two items are and that you will pass them around the group. Ask the children to hold one in each hand and decide which is heavier and which is lighter.

When the children have all decided ask: *How can we use the bucket balance to check?* Check that the children understand which bucket shows lighter and which shows heavier when the parcels are placed into the buckets.

Repeat this for other pairs of items.

No set answers

48 Comparing capacities

Learning objective Estimate, measure, weigh and compare objects, choosing and using suitable uniform non-standard or standard units and measuring instruments (eg a lever balance, metre stick or measuring jug). **Type of starter** Rehearse **Mental strategies** Children may think that the tallest or widest jug holds more. Show them that the tallest does not necessarily hold more. Repeat this for a wide, short jug.	**Resources** Jugs of different capacities; water or sand

Choose two jugs. Ask: *Which one do you think holds more? Why do you think that? How can we check?* Now pour some water into the jug which the children said holds more. Pour the water into the other jug until it is full. Ask: *Which jug holds more? Which one holds less?*

Repeat this for another pair of jugs. This time ask: *Which jug holds less?*

Now choose three jugs and ask the children to order them by which they think holds most/least. Check by pouring.

No set answers

BLOCK C

(49) **Car colours**

Resources
A chart similar to the one below for each group to complete and one for display purposes on a flipchart or interactive whiteboard

Learning objective
Answer a question by recording information in lists and tables.

Type of starter
Read

Mental strategies
Ask the children: *How do you know the answer? How did you work that out?* Encourage them to explain the mental process that they used.

No set answers

Favourite car colour	
Colour	**How many**
Red	
Blue	
Silver	
Black	

Ask the class: *If you could choose a car what colour would it be?* Split the class into groups and ask each group to complete the chart, with each child choosing their favourite car colour. There is space for them to write in other colours. When the lists are complete, enter the information on the large sheet, totalling how many votes there are for each colour. Now ask:

1.   Which is the most popular colour of car?

2.   Which colour is least popular?

3.   How many more silver cars are there than black ones?

4.   How many more... cars are there than... cars?

5.   How many fewer... cars are there than... cars?

Keep the display chart for use with Activity 51 Pictogram.

SCHOLASTIC

(50) Number sort

Learning objective Use diagrams to sort objects into groups according to a given criterion; suggest a different criterion for grouping the same objects. **Type of starter** Reason **Mental strategies** Ask the children to explain how they carried out the sorting. Check that the children understand how to sort into odd and even numbers. If children are unsure, use cubes to demonstrate that an even number can be broken into two equal parts.	**Resources** A large circle displayed on a flipchart or interactive whiteboard

Reveal the large circle. Explain to the children that you would like them to help you to sort some numbers.

Write the numbers 1 to 10 on the board.

Ask the children to sort the numbers so that they find all the even numbers. Say: *All the even numbers belong inside the circle.* Now ask:

1. Which numbers belong inside the circle?

2. Which even numbers are bigger than 5?

3. Which even numbers are between 3 and 7?

4. Which even numbers are smaller than 6?

Now ask the children to sort the numbers by their shape. Say that all the numbers that have a curve should go into the circle. Ask:

5. Which numbers go into the circle?

6. Which numbers have a curve and a straight line?

Now ask the children to suggest another way of sorting the numbers.

Answers

1.   2, 4, 6, 8, 10

2.   6, 8, 10

3.   4, 6

4.   2, 4

5.   2, 3, 5, 6, 8, 9, 0

6.   2, 5, 6, 9 (depending on font or handwriting style)

(51) **Pictogram**

Resources
Pictogram building software or a pictogram chart drawn on a flipchart (label the x-axis 'Car colour'); data from Activity 49 Car colours

Learning objective
Answer a question by recording information in lists and tables; present outcomes using practical resources, pictures, block graphs or pictograms.

Type of starter
Read

Mental strategies
Ask: *How do you know the answer? How did you work that out?* Encourage the children to explain the mental process that they used.

No set answers

Reveal the data from Activity 49 Car colours.

Explain to the children that you would like them to help you to build a pictogram from the data. Use one icon for each car and build the pictogram together.

When the pictogram is complete, hide the data chart. Then, using just the pictogram, ask:

1. How many cars are silver?

2. How many cars are red?

3. Are there more red cars than silver cars?

4. Are there fewer blue cars than black cars?

5. What is the difference between the silver cars and the black cars?

(52) **Sorting criteria**

Learning objective
Use diagrams to sort objects into groups according to a given criterion; suggest a different criterion for grouping the same objects.

Type of starter
Reason

Mental strategies
Encourage the children to use a mental number line to help them with the sorting. If they need further help, provide a number line so that they can track the numbers that they need on this.

Resources
Numeral cards 11–20 (from photocopiable page 89) for each child

Explain to the children that you will ask them to sort their numeral cards. Say:

1. Sort the cards so that you have all the numbers that have a 5 or a zero.

2. Sort the cards so that you have all the numbers that are between 11 and 16.

3. Sort the cards so that you have all the numbers between 14 and 19.

4. Sort the cards so that you have all the numbers that are larger than 15.

5. Sort the cards so that you have all the numbers that are less than 16 but more than 12.

Answers
1. 15 and 20
2. 12, 13, 14, 15
3. 15, 16, 17, 18
4. 16, 17, 18, 19, 20
5. 13, 14, 15

BLOCK C

(53) **Paper lengths**

Resources Strips of paper of varying lengths; cubes or sticks	**Learning objective** Estimate, measure, weigh and compare objects, choosing and using suitable uniform non-standard or standard units and measuring instruments (eg a lever balance, metre stick or measuring jug). **Type of starter** Rehearse **Mental strategies** Check that children understand that when making an estimate or measurement of length it is important to line the objects up, with one end of each object in line.

No set answers

Choose three strips of paper. Ask the children to look carefully at the strips and decide how they would order them by length.

Invite a child to demonstrate their ordering by placing the strips in order.

Ask:

1. How can we check that this is correct?

Invite three children to measure the strips using cubes or sticks. Say:

2. Now compare these three strips. How would you order them from longest to shortest?

Again, invite three children to measure the strips using non-standard uniform units such as cubes or sticks.

Repeat this again, this time putting four strips in order.

(54) Using non-standard units

BLOCK C

Learning objective

Estimate, measure, weigh and compare objects, choosing and using suitable uniform non-standard or standard units and measuring instruments (eg a lever balance, metre stick or measuring jug).

Type of starter

Recall

Mental strategies

Encourage the children to estimate how many of a unit will be needed to measure something. This can then be checked by a direct measure.

Resources

Non-standard uniform units such as cubes, sticks or pens

Show the children the first unit, such as a cube, and ask:

1. What could we measure with cubes?

2. Why would you measure... with cubes?

Invite a child to demonstrate how to measure something in the classroom with cubes. Discuss how important it is to line up the cubes with one end of the item to be measured.

Repeat this with other non-standard uniform units.

Now ask:

3. Why are sticks better for measuring... than cubes?

4. Why are cubes better for measuring... than sticks?

No set answers

(55) Zoo animals

Resources
A data collection chart for favourite zoo animals

Learning objective
Answer a question by recording information in lists and tables.

Type of starter
Read

Mental strategies
Ask the children to explain how they worked out their answers. Encourage them to use a mental number line to help them order the results. If children struggle with this, provide a number line to help them.

No set answers

Animal	How many
Lion	
Tiger	
Elephant	
Giraffe	
Monkey	
Penguin	
Sea lion	

Ask the children to put up their hands to show which is their favourite zoo animal from the chart. Count the hands for each animal, then write the total into the chart. Ask questions such as:

1. Which is the most popular animal?

2. Which animal is more popular than...?

3. Which animal is least popular?

4. How many more votes did... get than...?

5. How many fewer votes did... get than...?

(56) **Our pets**

Learning objective Answer a question by recording information in lists and tables; present outcomes using practical resources, pictures, block graphs or pictograms. **Type of starter** Read **Mental strategies** Children need to count up how many icons/cubes there are for each number of pets. They will need to point and count.	**Resources** Software to build a pictogram or cubes and a flipchart

Ask: *How many pets do you have?* Build a pictogram, with cubes or using software, to show how many pets the children have. Use one icon/cube to represent each child. Label the columns '1 pet', '2 pets' and so on. Ask:

No set answers

1. How many children have one pet?

2. How many children have four pets?

3. How many children have more than four pets?

4. What is the largest number of pets that someone has? How do you know that?

5. Do any children have no pets at all? How can you tell?

(57) **Estimate and check**

Learning objective Estimate, measure, weigh and compare objects, choosing and using suitable uniform non-standard or standard units and measuring instruments (eg a lever balance, metre stick or measuring jug). **Type of starter** Rehearse **Mental strategies** Ask the children to explain how they estimated. Check that they use what they learned from the first estimate and count in making subsequent estimates.	**Resources** Identical clear jars with 20, 15 and 30 cubes

Explain to the children that you will show them a jar with some cubes in it. Say:

No set answers

1. How many cubes do you think are in the jar?

2. James, please count how many cubes there are.

3. Did you make a good estimate?

Repeat this for the other jars.

BLOCK C

(58) **Box measuring**

Resources
A transparent plastic box about 20cm long; cubes; a bucket balance; sand or water; scoops

Learning objective
Estimate, measure, weigh and compare objects, choosing and using suitable uniform non-standard or standard units and measuring instruments (eg a lever balance, metre stick or measuring jug).

Type of starter
Rehearse

Mental strategies
Encourage the children to make reasonable estimates. Ask: *How did you decide what your estimate should be?*

No set answers

Tell the children that you would like them to explain how to find the length of the box. Say:

1. Here are some cubes. How many cubes do you think will be needed to measure the length of the box?

2. Sally, show us how to put the cubes down in order to measure the box. How many cubes long is the box?

Check that the cubes are laid alongside the box, with the first one abutting the end of the box and the cubes placed tightly together in a straight line.

Now repeat this for the weight of the box.

3. Take turns to hold the box. How many cubes do you think the box weighs?

4. Paul, show us how to weigh the box with cubes. How many cubes does the box weigh?

Observe whether the child checks that the bucket balance is in balance before it is used.

Now repeat this for capacity.

5. How many scoops of sand do you think the box will hold?

6. Chelsea, show us how to use scoops of sand to find the box's capacity. How many scoops did you need?

Observe whether each scoop of sand is about the same – that some are not piled high, while others are half empty.

(59) Counting pattern sort

Learning objective
Use diagrams to sort objects into groups according to a given criterion.

Type of starter
Reason

Mental strategies
Encourage the children to count in their heads. Some children may count aloud. If so, encourage them to do this very quietly. If children are unsure, count aloud together.

Resources
Numeral cards 0–20 (enlarged from photocopiable pages 88 and 89); a circle on a flipchart into which numbers can be sorted; sticky-tack

Ask the children to help you sort the numbers 0 to 20. Stick the number into the circle on the flipchart each time. Say:

1. Count in twos starting from zero. Sort out those number cards.

2. What is special about these numbers?

3. What do we call the numbers that are left?

4. Now count in fives starting from zero. Sort out those number cards.

5. What do you notice about these numbers?

6. Which of these numbers comes in the count of tens?

7. What would the next number be in the count of tens?

Answers

1. 0, 2, 4, 6, 8, 10, 12, 14, 16, 18, 20

2. even numbers

3. odd numbers

4. 0, 5, 10, 15, 20

5. they end with a 0 or 5 in their units

6. 0, 10, 20

7. 30

BLOCK C

(60) **Shape sort**

Resources
Simple Carroll diagrams for each pair; 3D shape models of a sphere, cube, cuboid, pyramid and cone for each pair

Learning objective
Use diagrams to sort objects into groups according to a given criterion.

Type of starter
Reason

Mental strategies
If children are unsure about where a shape fits, ask them to examine the shape carefully, holding it in their hands, and feeling the edges, faces and any curves.

Answers

1. cube, cuboid, pyramid

2. sphere, cone

3. cube, cuboid

4. cube, cuboid, sphere, cone

5. sphere, cone

Reveal the first Carroll diagram.

Has straight edges	Does not have straight edges

Explain that you would like the children to sort the shapes by the properties on the diagram. Say:

1. Sort the shapes by 'Has straight edges'.

2. Which shapes go into the 'Does not have straight edges' section?

Now provide other Carroll diagrams for these questions:

3. Sort the shapes by 'Has six faces'. Which shapes are these?

4. Sort the shapes by 'Has triangular faces'. Which shapes do not have triangular faces?

5. Sort the shapes by 'Has curved faces'. Which shapes are these?

BLOCK D

Unit 1

	100 Mental Maths Starters			100 Maths Lessons		
Page	Objective	Activity title	Starter type	Unit	Lesson	Page
59	Visualise and use everyday language to describe the position of objects and direction and distance when moving them, for example when placing or moving objects on a game board.	**61** I spy	Rehearse	1	2	138, 139
59	Count reliably at least 20 objects, recognising that when rearranged the number of objects stays the same.	**62** Counting up to 20	Refresh	3	3	139
60	Count reliably at least 20 objects, recognising that when rearranged the number of objects stays the same; estimate a number of objects that can be checked by counting.	**63** Estimate and count	Refresh	3	4	140
60	Use vocabulary related to time; order days of the week and months.	**64** Days of the week	Recall	1	6	146
61	Use vocabulary related to time; order days of the week and months.	**65** Our day	Rehearse	1	7, 8	142, 143
61	Estimate, measure, weigh and compare objects, choosing and using suitable uniform non-standard or standard units and measuring instruments (eg a lever balance, metre stick or measuring jug).	**66** Choosing appropriate units	Reason	1	9, 10	143, 144

Unit 2

	100 Mental Maths Starters			100 Maths Lessons		
Page	Objective	Activity title	Starter type	Unit	Lesson	Page
62	Solve problems involving counting, adding, subtracting, doubling or halving in the context of numbers, measures or money, for example to 'pay' and 'give change'.	**67** Shopping	Rehearse	2	1	150
63	Relate addition to counting on; recognise that addition can be done in any order; use practical and informal written methods to support the addition of a one-digit number or a multiple of 10 to a one-digit or two-digit number.	**68** Partitioning	Refine	2	2	150
64	Understand subtraction as 'take away' and find a 'difference' by counting up; use practical and informal written methods to support the subtraction of a one-digit number from a one-digit or two-digit number and a multiple of 10 from a two-digit number.	**69** Counting on (subtraction)	Refine	2	3	150

Unit 2 ...continued

	100 Mental Maths Starters			**100 Maths Lessons**		
Page	**Objective**	**Activity title**	**Starter type**	**Unit**	**Lesson**	**Page**
64	Understand subtraction as 'take away' and find a 'difference' by counting up; use practical and informal written methods to support the subtraction of a one-digit number from a one-digit or two-digit number and a multiple of 10 from a two-digit number.	70 How many more fingers?	Refine	2	4	151, 152
65	Use vocabulary related to time; order days of the week and months.	71 Which day?	Recall	2	7	154
65	Use vocabulary related to time; order days of the week and months; read the time to the hour and half hour.	72 What's the time?	Read	2	8	155

Unit 3

	100 Mental Maths Starters			**100 Maths Lessons**		
Page	**Objective**	**Activity title**	**Starter type**	**Unit**	**Lesson**	**Page**
66	Relate addition to counting on; recognise that addition can be done in any order; use practical and informal written methods to support the addition of a one-digit number or a multiple of 10 to a one-digit or two-digit number.	73 Partitioning to add	Refine	3	1	162
66	Relate addition to counting on; recognise that addition can be done in any order; use practical and informal written methods to support the addition of a one-digit number or a multiple of 10 to a one-digit or two-digit number.	74 Bridging 10	Refine	3	2	163
67	Relate addition to counting on; recognise that addition can be done in any order; use practical and informal written methods to support the addition of a one-digit number or a multiple of 10 to a one-digit or two-digit number.	75 Bridging 10 and 20	Refine	3	4	163, 164
68	Understand subtraction as 'take away' and find a 'difference' by counting up; use practical and informal written methods to support the subtraction of a one-digit number from a one-digit or two-digit number and a multiple of 10 from a two-digit number.	76 Subtraction	Refine	3	5	164, 165
69	Use vocabulary related to time; order days of the week and months; read the time to the hour and half hour.	77 Telling the time	Read	3	8	167
69	Visualise and use everyday language to describe the position of objects and direction and distance when moving them, for example when placing or moving objects on a game board.	78 Position and movement	Rehearse	3	9, 10	167, 168

(61) I spy

Learning objective Visualise and use everyday language to describe the position of objects and direction and distance when moving them, for example when placing or moving objects on a game board. **Type of starter** Rehearse **Mental strategies** Check that the children understand the language being used.	**Resources** None
Play 'I spy'. Say: *I spy with my little eye something on top… inside… underneath… behind… beside… the table… the chair… the cupboard…* and so on. Keep the pace of this sharp and when the children are confident with this game of position, they can take turns to say 'I spy…'.	**No set answers**

(62) Counting up to 20

Learning objective Count reliably at least 20 objects, recognising that when rearranged the number of objects stays the same. **Type of starter** Refresh **Mental strategies** Check that the children count either by touching, moving and saying the counting number or by touching and saying the number. Check that the last number they say is the number that they give for the count.	**Resources** An A4 sheet of coloured paper for each child; 20 items for each child to count, such as cubes, counters or buttons
Explain that you would like the children to use the sheet of paper as a counting mat. As they put out the cubes for counting, they must count them on the mat. Say: 1. Take a handful of cubes. Put them onto the mat. Count them. How many do you have? 2. Now count out 8… 10… 15… cubes. 3. Ask your partner to check how many cubes you counted out.	**No set answers**

BLOCK D

(63) Estimate and count

Resources 20 items for each child to count, such as counters or buttons; a recording sheet for each child	**Learning objective** Count reliably at least 20 objects, recognising that when rearranged the number of objects stays the same; estimate a number of objects that can be checked by counting. **Type of starter** Refresh **Mental strategies** Check that the estimates are reasonably accurate and that children are learning from one turn to the next about the approximate amount of counters that they need. Check that the children count either by touching, moving and saying the counting number or by touching and saying the number. Check that the last number they say is the number that they give for the count.
No set answers	Each child needs a recording sheet with the headings 'Estimate' and 'Count'. Organise the children to work in pairs. They take turns to take a handful of counters that they estimate is the number that you say. They count them and their partner checks. They should record the number to be estimated and their count. Say: 1. Estimate 3... 9... 12... 16... 20... 14... counters. 2. Now count them.

(64) Days of the week

Resources A set of cards each with a day of the week written on and sticky-tacked to the flipchart in order	**Learning objective** Use vocabulary related to time; order days of the week and months. **Type of starter** Recall **Mental strategies** Children may have difficulty in recognising the name of the day before. Say the day names together in order. Stop on a day and ask: *Which day comes before...?* Repetition over time helps children to build a mental picture of the days and their order.
No set answers	Recite together the days of the week, in order. Remove the cards from the flipchart and shuffle them. Hold up a card. Ask: *Which day of the week is this?* Invite the child who answers to come out and hold the card. Repeat for the other cards. Ask the class to order the children so the days of the week are in order. Collect in the cards. Ask questions such as: 1. Which day of the week is today? 2. Which day will be tomorrow? 3. Which day was yesterday? 4. Which day comes after/before Sunday?

(65) Our day

	Resources
Learning objective Use vocabulary related to time; order days of the week and months. **Type of starter** Rehearse **Mental strategies** Children need to order their day and think back and forth through the day. If they are unsure, go slowly through the day, starting from when they wake up.	**Resources** None

Explain that you will ask the children some questions about the day. Ask them to answer in sentences. Say, for example:

1. What time is lunch?

2. What did you do as soon as you got to school today?

3. What will we do after our maths lesson?

4. What happened before our maths lesson?

5. What time shall we finish school today?

6. What are you going to do when you go home?

No set answers

(66) Choosing appropriate units

	Resources
Learning objective Estimate, measure, weigh and compare objects, choosing and using suitable uniform non-standard or standard units and measuring instruments (eg a lever balance, metre stick or measuring jug). **Type of starter** Reason **Mental strategies** Check that the children make a reasonable choice of unit and can explain why they made that choice. Check that for capacity they understand that the height of the jug does not give its capacity, that they need to look at the jug in terms of height and width.	**Resources** A bucket balance; cubes, uniform sticks, counters; parcels of differing weights and sizes; containers of different capacities and heights; scoops; sand

Choose a parcel and ask the children to decide which unit they would choose to measure its length. Invite a child to demonstrate this. Ask:

1. Was this a good unit to choose?

2. Why do you think that?

3. Naomi, measure the parcel with the chosen unit please.

Repeat this for other parcels for length. Then ask the children to feel the weight of one of the parcels and decide which unit they would use to weigh it. Repeat the activity for weight.

Repeat this for capacity, using a jug and scoops of sand.

No set answers

BLOCK D

(67) **Shopping**

Resources Pots of coins for each pair: 1p, 2p, 5p, 10p, 20p	**Learning objective** Solve problems involving counting, adding, subtracting, doubling or halving in the context of numbers, measures or money, for example to 'pay' and 'give change'. **Type of starter** Rehearse **Mental strategies** The coins will help the shopkeeper to count up the change. This will help the children to build a mental image of counting on using coins, as if counting on a number line. More confident children may just count up in their heads then count out the appropriate change. Encourage these children to give the fewest number of coins possible.
No set answers	Ask the children to work in pairs. They take turns to be the shopkeeper. The other child is the customer. Explain that you will give the customers amounts to spend and tell them which coins to use. The shopkeeper should count out the change using the 'shopkeeper's method' of counting on, using coins. For example, change from 10p for a 6p spend would be '6p and 2p makes 8p and 2p makes 10p'. So the change is 4p. Say: 1. Spend 7p and give the shopkeeper 10p. 2. Spend 4p and give the shopkeeper 10p. 3. Spend 15p and give the shopkeeper 20p. 4. Spend 13p and give the shopkeeper 20p. 5. Spend 11p and give the shopkeeper 20p.

(68) Partitioning

Learning objective
Relate addition to counting on; recognise that addition can be done in any order; use practical and informal written methods to support the addition of a one-digit number or a multiple of 10 to a one-digit or two-digit number.

Type of starter
Refine

Resources
Nine interlocking cubes for each child; a board or flipchart

Ask the children to make a tower of seven cubes.

Explain that they are going to make 'five and a bit' from this tower. They should count five into one tower and then count how many are left. Ask: *How many more cubes are there than five?*

Say: *We made five, and two more, from seven.* Repeat this together.

Practise making 'five and a bit' from:

1. eight cubes
2. six cubes
3. nine cubes

Write 5 + 7 on the board. Remind the children that they can make 'five and a bit' to help them add numbers together. Ask for suggestions. Encourage the response: 5 + 5 + 2 = 10 + 2 = 12.

4. 5 + 8
5. 5 + 6
6. 5 + 9

Answers
1. five and three
2. five and one
3. five and four

4. 13
5. 11
6. 14

(69) Counting on (subtraction)

Resources
A number snake
0–20 (from
photocopiable page
94) for each child

Learning objective
Understand subtraction as 'take away' and find a 'difference' by counting up; use practical and informal written methods to support the subtraction of a one-digit number from a one-digit or two-digit number and a multiple of 10 from a two-digit number.

Type of starter
Refine

Mental strategies
After each question, ask: *How many did you count on?* or *How many steps did you take?*

Answers

1. 5
2. 5
3. 2
4. 6
5. 5
6. 5
7. 5
8. 9
9. 6
10. 4

Ask the children to count on each time from the first number to the second in order to find out how many 'steps' they have taken. They must put a finger on the first number they have said and count on as they move the finger to the second number.

Count on from...

1.	3 to 8	6.	6 to 11
2.	5 to 10	7.	9 to 14
3.	2 to 4	8.	7 to 16
4.	1 to 7	9.	4 to 10
5.	4 to 9	10.	8 to 12

(70) How many more fingers?

Resources
None

Learning objective
Understand subtraction as 'take away' and find a 'difference' by counting up; use practical and informal written methods to support the subtraction of a one-digit number from a one-digit or two-digit number and a multiple of 10 from a two-digit number.

Type of starter Refine

Answers

1. 5
2. 7
3. 2
4. 6
5. 3
6. 9

Ask the children to show ten fingers, then six fingers. *How many more fingers are needed to make 10?* Count together from 6 to 10.

Ask the children to use their fingers to show you the other number needed to make 10: *How many from... to make 10?*

1	5	4.	4
2.	3	5.	7
3.	8	6.	1

100 MENTAL MATHS ACTIVITIES · YEAR 1   ■SCHOLASTIC

(71) Which day?

Learning objective
Use vocabulary related to time; order days of the week and months.

Type of starter
Recall

Mental strategies
Children need to use a mental image of the days of the week in order. If children are unsure, say the days of the week in order together and pin up a set of days of the week cards to act as an aid.

Resources
Days of the week cards for each child (these can be made using a word processor or printed from the Numeracy Framework CD-ROM of vocabulary)

Ask the children to spread their cards out in front of them in day order. Now explain that you will ask questions about the days of the week and will ask the children to hold up the relevant card when you say *Show me*. Say:

1. Which day is it today? Show me.
2. Which day will it be tomorrow? Show me.
3. Which day was it yesterday? Show me.
4. Which day comes after Tuesday? Show me.
5. Which day is next after Saturday? Show me.
6. Which day is before Thursday? Show me.

No set answers

(72) What's the time?

Learning objective
Use vocabulary related to time; order days of the week and months; read the time to the hour and half hour.

Type of starter
Read

Resources
A teaching clock

Ask the children to tell you the times as you show them on the clock face.

1.	2 o'clock	4.	8 o'clock
2.	5 o'clock	5.	10 o'clock
3.	1 o'clock	6.	6 o'clock

Ask: *What time is it?* as you show the children 9 o'clock, then half past 9. If necessary, explain that half past 9 is half an hour after 9 o'clock.

Ask: *What time is it?*

7.	3 o'clock	10.	half past 7
8.	half past 3	11.	11 o'clock
9.	7 o'clock	12.	half past 11

No set answers

BLOCK D

(73) **Partitioning to add**

Resources	Learning objective
A board or flipchart	Relate addition to counting on; recognise that addition can be done in any order; use practical and informal written methods to support the addition of a one-digit number or a multiple of 10 to a one-digit or two-digit number.

Type of starter
Refine

Answers

1. 12
2. 14
3. 14
4. 15

Remind the children of the strategy of partitioning larger numbers into '5 and a bit', recombining to make 10, then counting on. Write: 5 + 8 = .

Ask: *How can we do this?* Encourage the partitioning and recombining strategy. Write: 5 + 8 = 5 + 5 + 3 = 10 + 3 = 13.

Emphasise that 5 + 5 = 10, and that adding on to 10 is easy!

Write each example on the board and ask an individual to explain how he or she is going to work it out.

1. 5 + 7   2. 5 + 9

Write: 6 + 7 = . Ask for suggestions about how to find the answer. Write: 5 + 1 + 5 + 2. Encourage adding the fives first to make 10, then adding the ones: 6 + 7 = 5 + 1 + 5 + 2 = 10 + 3 = 13.

3. 8 + 6   4. 7 + 8

(74) **Bridging 10**

Resources	Learning objective
A board or flipchart	Relate addition to counting on; recognise that addition can be done in any order; use practical and informal written methods to support the addition of a one-digit number or a multiple of 10 to a one-digit or two-digit number.

Type of starter
Refine

Mental strategies
Remind the children of the strategy for adding two numbers when the answer will cross through 10. Stress that they are looking to make 10 because adding on to 10 is easy!

Answers

1. 12
2. 16
3. 13
4. 12
5. 14

Write: 6 + 7.

Ask for the answer and how the children worked it out. Collect several methods. Encourage making 10: 6 + 7 = 6 + 4 + 3 = 10 + 3 = 13.

Write each example and ask an individual how he or she is going to find the answer.

1. 4 + 8   4. 5 + 7
2. 7 + 9   5. 9 + 5
3. 7 + 6

BLOCK D

(75) Bridging 10 and 20

Learning objective
Relate addition to counting on; recognise that addition can be done in any order; use practical and informal written methods to support the addition of a one-digit number or a multiple of 10 to a one-digit or two-digit number.

Type of starter
Refine

Resources
A board or flipchart

Write: 18 + 5 = .

Ask: *How can we work it out?* Encourage the children to suggest methods, such as: '18 add 2 is 20, and add 3 more is 23'.

Write: 18 + 5 = 18 + 2 + 3 = 20 + 3 = 23.

Remind the children that they are trying to make 20 because adding on to 20 is easy!

Write each of the examples in turn, and ask an individual to say the answer and explain how he or she worked it out. Write out each partitioned equation in full, as above.

1.   17 + 8

2.   15 + 7

3.   16 + 6

4.   19 + 4

5.   18 + 6

Answers

1.   25

2.   22

3.   22

4.   23

5.   24

BLOCK D

⑦⑥ **Subtraction**

Resources
Individual whiteboards and pens

Learning objective

Understand subtraction as 'take away' and find a 'difference' by counting up; use practical and informal written methods to support the subtraction of a one-digit number from a one-digit or two-digit number and a multiple of 10 from a two-digit number.

Type of starter

Refine

Mental strategies

Children can count on from the lower to the higher number, using a mental number line to help them.

For questions where a one-digit number is taken away from a two-digit number they can use facts they already know, such as for 15 – 4: 5 – 4 = 1 so 15 – 4 is 11.

Where the subtraction crosses the tens boundary, such as 14 – 9, they can break this down: 14 – 9 = 10 + 4 – 9 = 1 + 4 = 5.

For subtracting multiples of ten from a two-digit number they can count back the number of tens. For example, 56 – 40: 46; 36; 26; 16.

Answers

1. 7
2. 3
3. 15
4. 15
5. 7
6. 13
7. 26

Explain to the children that you will ask them some subtraction questions. Ask them to find the answer. They can use their whiteboards to write down number sentences to help them, if they need to. They must write the answer and when you say *Show me* they hold up their whiteboards. Ask the children how they worked out the answer.

Say, for example:

1. What is 13 subtract 6?

2. What is the difference between 16 and 13?

3. What is 19 take away 4?

4. What is 18 take away 3?

5. What is 15 – 8?

6. What is 23 take away 10?

7. What is 46 take away 20?

(77) Telling the time

Learning objective
Use vocabulary related to time; order days of the week and months; read the time to the hour and half hour.

Type of starter
Read

Resources
A teaching clock

Ask the children to tell you the times as you show them on the clock face.

1.   4 o'clock
2.   half past 4
3.   12 o'clock
4.   9 o'clock

5.   half past 2
6.   half past 5
7.   half past 10
8.   6 o'clock

Ask questions 9-12 without demonstrating them on the clock.

9.   How long is it from 6 o'clock to 7 o'clock?
10. How long is it from 3 o'clock to 4 o'clock?
11. How long is it from 6 o'clock to 8 o'clock?
12. How long is it from half past 2 to half past 3?

Answers
9.   1 hour
10. 1 hour

11. 2 hours
12. 1 hour

(78) Position and movement

Learning objective
Visualise and use everyday language to describe the position of objects and direction and distance when moving them, for example when placing or moving objects on a game board.

Type of starter
Rehearse

Resources
A large space such as the hall or outside

Ask the children to spread out. Explain that you will give instructions for them to follow. Say:

1.   Move three steps forward.
2.   Turn to your right.
3.   Move back five steps.
4.   Turn to your left.
5.   Move forward six paces.

No set answers

Repeat this for other similar moves, checking that the children understand the vocabulary of position and movement by observing how they move and where they stop.

Now ask them to work in pairs to give each other instructions similar to those in the group activity.

BLOCK E

Unit 1

100 Mental Maths Starters				100 Maths Lessons		
Page	Objective	Activity title	Starter type	Unit	Lesson	Page
72	Count on or back in ones, twos, fives and tens and use this knowledge to derive the multiples of 2, 5 and 10 to the tenth multiple.	**79** Counting to 20 and back	Recall	1	1	173, 174
72	Count on or back in ones, twos, fives and tens and use this knowledge to derive the multiples of 2, 5 and 10 to the tenth multiple.	**80** Counting from a small number	Recall	1	3	175
73	Count on or back in ones, twos, fives and tens and use this knowledge to derive the multiples of 2, 5 and 10 to the tenth multiple.	**81** Odd or even	Recall	1	5	176
73	Count on or back in ones, twos, fives and tens and use this knowledge to derive the multiples of 2, 5 and 10 to the tenth multiple.	**82** Counting in tens	Recall	1	2	174
74	Recall the doubles of all numbers to at least 10.	**83** Matching doubles	Recall	1	7	177
74	Recall the doubles of all numbers to at least 10.	**84** Numeral doubles	Rehearse	1	8	178
75	Use the vocabulary related to addition and subtraction and symbols to describe and record addition and subtraction number sentences.	**85** Missing numbers	Read	1	11	179
75	Use the vocabulary related to addition and subtraction and symbols to describe and record addition and subtraction number sentences.	**86** Trios	Read	1	15	181

Unit 2

100 Mental Maths Starters				100 Maths Lessons		
Page	Objective	Activity title	Starter type	Unit	Lesson	Page
76	Use the vocabulary related to addition and subtraction and symbols to describe and record addition and subtraction number sentences.	**87** Addition sentences	Read	2	1	189, 190
77	Solve problems involving counting, adding, subtracting, doubling or halving in the context of numbers, measures or money, for example to 'pay' and 'give change'.	**88** At the shop	Rehearse	2	2	190, 191
77	Count on or back in ones, twos, fives and tens and use this knowledge to derive the multiples of 2, 5 and 10 to the tenth multiple.	**89** Counting patterns	Recall	2	8	194

Unit 2 ...continued

	100 Mental Maths Starters			100 Maths Lessons		
Page	Objective	Activity title	Starter type	Unit	Lesson	Page
78	Use the vocabulary related to addition and subtraction and symbols to describe and record addition and subtraction number sentences.	90 Subtraction sentences	Read	2	3	191
79	Count on or back in ones, twos, fives and tens and use this knowledge to derive the multiples of 2, 5 and 10 to the tenth multiple.	91 Counting in twos	Recall	2	8	194
79	Recall the doubles of all numbers to at least 10.	92 Doubles snap	Recall	2	11	196
80	Use the vocabulary of halves and quarters in context.	93 Halves and quarters	Rehearse	2	12	197
81	Solve practical problems that involve combining groups of 2, 5 or 10, or sharing into equal groups.	94 Groups of 2 and 5	Rehearse	2	14	198

Unit 3

	100 Mental Maths Starters			100 Maths Lessons		
Page	Objective	Activity title	Starter type	Unit	Lesson	Page
82	Count on or back in ones, twos, fives and tens and use this knowledge to derive the multiples of 2, 5 and 10 to the tenth multiple.	95 Count in ones and tens	Recall	3	1	207, 208
82	Count on or back in ones, twos, fives and tens and use this knowledge to derive the multiples of 2, 5 and 10 to the tenth multiple.	96 Count in tens	Recall	3	3	208
83	Recall the doubles of all numbers to at least 10.	97 Doubles	Recall	3	6	210
84	Count on or back in ones, twos, fives and tens and use this knowledge to derive the multiples of 2, 5 and 10 to the tenth multiple.	98 Count in twos and fives	Recall	3	4	209
84	Use the vocabulary of halves and quarters in context.	99 Quarters	Rehearse	2	7	211
85	Solve practical problems that involve combining groups of 2, 5 or 10, or sharing into equal groups.	100 Combining groups of 2	Refine	3	8	211
86	Solve practical problems that involve combining groups of 2, 5 or 10, or sharing into equal groups.	101 Groups of 5 and 10	Refine	3	9	211, 212
87	Solve practical problems that involve combining groups of 2, 5 or 10, or sharing into equal groups.	102 Groups of 2, 5 and 10	Rehearse	3	9	211, 212

BLOCK E

(79) **Counting to 20 and back**

Resources None	**Learning objective** Count on or back in ones, twos, fives and tens and use this knowledge to derive the multiples of 2, 5 and 10 to the tenth multiple. **Type of starter** Recall
No set answers	Get the children to sit in a circle. Ask them to count with you from 1 to 10 and back again, then from 1 to 20 and back again. Count around the circle from 1 to 10, then back again, until everyone has had two turns. Repeat for 1 to 20 and back again. Now encourage the children to clap to congratulate each other.

(80) **Counting from a small number**

Resources Numeral cards 1–10 (enlarged from photocopiable page 88)	**Learning objective** Count on or back in ones, twos, fives and tens and use this knowledge to derive the multiples of 2, 5 and 10 to the tenth multiple. **Type of starter** Recall
No set answers	Ask the children to sit in a circle. Ask them to count with you from 1 to 20 and back again. Tell the children that they have to count to 20 and back from a small number (such as 5). Ask a child to hold up the '5' card for everyone to see. Repeat, counting from other small numbers:

1. 7
2. 3
3. 8

4. 4
5. 2

(81) Odd or even

Learning objective
Count on or back in ones, twos, fives and tens and use this knowledge to derive the multiples of 2, 5 and 10 to the tenth multiple.

Type of starter
Recall

Resources
Numeral cards 1–10 (enlarged from photocopiable page 88)

Give out the cards and build a number line, with each child holding a card. Count together. Ask the child with the '1' card to kneel, and then every other child, until all the odd numbers are kneeling and the evens standing.

Count together in twos from 2. Explain that these are called even numbers. Count together in twos from 1. Explain that these are odd numbers. Then, count together from 1 to 10, shouting the odd numbers and whispering the even numbers.

Ask whether the following numbers are odd or even, and how the children know (for example, 'I said "4" when I counted in twos from 2').

1.	8	5.	1
2.	5	6.	4
3.	3	7.	2
4.	6	8.	7

Answers
1. even
2. odd
3. odd
4. even
5. odd
6. even
7. even
8. odd

(82) Counting in tens

Learning objective
Count on or back in ones, twos, fives and tens and use this knowledge to derive the multiples of 2, 5 and 10 to the tenth multiple.

Type of starter
Recall

Resources
A tens number line 0–100 (from photocopiable page 92) for each child

Ask the children to point to each number as they count in tens from 0 to 100 and back.

Start at 30 and count on 4 tens. Ask: *Where have we counted to?*

For questions 6–10, explain to the children that they are going to take tens away. Stress that the answer will be a smaller number.

1.	Start at 20, count on 3 tens	6.	Start at 70, take 2 tens away
2.	Start at 50, count on 2 tens	7.	Start at 40, take 1 ten away
3.	Start at 80, count on 1 ten	8.	Start at 90, take 7 tens away
4.	Start at 30, count on 4 tens	9.	Start at 60, take 5 tens away
5.	Start at 60, count on 3 tens	10.	Start at 80, take 4 tens away

Answers
1. 50
2. 70
3. 90
4. 70
5. 90
6. 50
7. 30
8. 20
9. 10
10. 40

(83) Matching doubles

Resources	**Learning objective**
Numeral cards 1-10 (photocopiable page 88); a washing line (or string) and pegs; a set of 'Domino doubles' cards (enlarged from photocopiable page 93)	Recall the doubles of all numbers to at least 10.
	Type of starter
	Recall

No set answers

Give out the numeral cards. Place the domino cards face down. Ask a child who is not holding a numeral card to choose a domino card (for example, double 3) and hold it up for all to see.

The child with the matching numeral card (6) stands next to the first child. They say together: 'Double 3 is 6.' The class repeats this.

Continue until all the domino cards have been used at least twice.

Ask the children whose numeral cards have not been used to peg their cards on the line in order. Tell the children that these numbers are called odd numbers. Say them together: 1, 3, 5, 7, 9.

(84) Numeral doubles

Resources	**Learning objective**
Numeral cards 1-20 (enlarged from photocopiable pages 88 and 89)	Recall the doubles of all numbers to at least 10.
	Type of starter
	Rehearse

Answers

1. 4
2. 10
3. 6
4. 16
5. 20
6. 12
7. 2
8. 8
9. 14
10. 18

Spread the numeral cards face up on the carpet. Ask an individual to choose the card that is the answer to each question and stand with it in front of the class.

1.	What is double 2?	6.	double 6
2.	5 add 5	7.	What is double 1?
3.	double 3	8.	double 4
4.	8 add 8	9.	7 add 7
5.	double 10	10.	double 9

When all the questions have been answered, ask the children who are holding up the cards to stand in order. What do the children notice about these numbers? They may say that 'some are missing' or 'they are every other number'. Explain that these numbers are called even numbers. Say the even numbers from 2 to 20 together.

(85) Missing numbers

Learning objective
Use the vocabulary related to addition and subtraction and symbols to describe and record addition and subtraction number sentences.

Type of starter
Read

Resources
'Make 10' cards (enlarged from photocopiable page 95); numeral cards 0–10 (enlarged from photocopiable page 88) for each child

No set answers

Explain that you will hold up a card with a number sentence on it that totals 10, but has one number missing (for example, 7 + ☐ = 10). Ask the children to read the card with you, saying 'How many?' for the missing number. They should hold up a numeral card to show their answer.

Say the number sentence together (for example, '7 add 3 equals 10').

(86) Trios

Learning objective
Use the vocabulary related to addition and subtraction and symbols to describe and record addition and subtraction number sentences.

Type of starter
Read

Resources
Numeral cards 0–10 and signs +, – and = (enlarged from photocopiable pages 88 and 89); a board or flipchart

No set answers

Choose five children to hold up the cards:

| 2 | 3 | 5 | + | = |

Ask them to stand in order to make an addition statement (such as: 2 + 3 = 5). Ask: *Can we make a different addition statement?* (3 + 2 = 5)

Replace the + sign with a – and ask the children to make a subtraction statement. Ask: *Can we make a different 'take away'?* Discuss why 2 – 5 = 3 is not correct.

Write the four statements on the board and say them together.

Repeat the activity with:

1. 6   2   4

2. 3   5   8

3. 7   4   3

4. 4   9   5

5. 2   8   10

Addition sentences

Resources
Individual whiteboards and pens

Learning objective
Use the vocabulary related to addition and subtraction and symbols to describe and record addition and subtraction number sentences.

Type of starter
Read

Mental strategies
Check that the children work mentally. Some will 'know' the answers to some of these additions. Where they use mental methods to work out the answer, ask children to explain what they have done. Invite a child each time to read out their number sentence and show it to the class.

Answers

1. $5 + 4 = 9$
2. $6 + 3 = 9$
3. $9 + 1 = 10$
4. $3 + 4 = 7$
5. $4 + 6 = 10$
6. $4 + 5 = 9$
7. $3 + 5 = 8$
8. $4 + 2 = 6$
9. $9 + 2 = 11$
10. $6 + 10 = 16$

Explain that you will say an addition sentence. Ask the children to write the addition as a number sentence, along with the answer. When you say *Show me* the children must hold up their whiteboards for you to see.

Questions 6-10 are word problems. Ask the children to write the number sentence and answer as before.

1.   What is $5 + 4$?

2.   What is $6 + 3$?

3.   What is $9 + 1$?

4.   What is $3 + 4$?

5.   What is $4 + 6$?

6.   Sara has four beads. Ruth gives her five more. How many beads has Sara now?

7.   Mark has three marbles. He buys another five marbles. How many marbles does Mark have in total?

8.   There are four kittens in the kitchen. There are two kittens in the hall. How many kittens are there altogether?

9.   Nine dogs are in their kennels. Two dogs are running around outside. How many dogs are there in total?

10. Six swans are swimming on the lake. Ten swans are sitting on the grass. How many swans are there altogether?

(88) **At the shop**

Learning objective Solve problems involving counting, adding, subtracting, doubling or halving in the context of numbers, measures or money, for example to 'pay' and 'give change'. **Type of starter** Rehearse **Mental strategies** Encourage the children to work mentally, using an imaginary number line.	**Resources** A set of price labels from 1p to 20p, shuffled; a pot of 1p, 2p, 5p, 10p and 20p coins for each pair

Explain that you will hold up a price label. Ask the children to decide which coin they would use to pay. They must choose a coin larger than the price. Now ask the children to work out the change, again working mentally by counting up, using coins to help them. Keep the pace sharp. Ask:	**No set answers**

1. Which coin would you choose to pay?
2. Why did you choose that coin?
3. How much change will you receive?
4. How did you work that out?
5. Which coins would you choose to give the change?
6. Which coins can you use so that you use the least number of coins?

(89) **Counting patterns**

Learning objective Count on or back in ones, twos, fives and tens and use this knowledge to derive the multiples of 2, 5 and 10 to the tenth multiple. **Type of starter** Recall	**Resources** None

Ask the children to sit in a circle. Count together from zero to 20, then back to zero. Count around the circle, forwards and backwards. Count together from a small number up to 20 and back to zero. Repeat, this time counting around the circle, until everyone has had at least two turns. Start numbers:	**No set answers**

1. 5
2. 3
3. 7
4. 4
5. 8

BLOCK E

 Subtraction sentences

Resources	Learning objective
Individual whiteboards and pens	Use the vocabulary related to addition and subtraction and symbols to describe and record addition and subtraction number sentences.

Type of starter
Read

Mental strategies
Encourage the children to use a mental number line to count up from the smaller to larger number. For some questions, the children may 'know' the answer. For questions 6-10, the children will find it helpful to use facts they already know to find the answer.

Answers

1. $9 - 3 = 6$
2. $8 - 4 = 4$
3. $10 - 7 = 3$
4. $9 - 6 = 3$
5. $12 - 2 = 10$
6. $8 - 3 = 5$
7. $7 - 6 = 1$
8. $10 - 4 = 6$
9. $15 - 13 = 2$
10. $19 - 16 = 3$

Explain that you will say a subtraction sentence. Ask the children to write the subtraction as a number sentence, along with the answer. When you say *Show me* the children must hold up their whiteboards for you to see.

Questions 6-10 are word problems. Ask the children to write the number sentence and answer as before.

1. What is 9 subtract 3?

2. What does 8 take away 4 leave?

3. What is the difference between 7 and 10?

4. How much more is 9 than 6?

5. What is 12 take away 2?

6. Sam has eight sweets. He eats three. How many sweets does Sam have left?

7. Shona has seven cards. Sanjay has six cards. How many fewer cards does Sanjay have?

8. Ten pigeons sit on the roof. Four fly away. How many pigeons are left on the roof?

9. Thirteen ducks swim in the pond. Fifteen ducks sit on the grass. How many more ducks are sitting on the grass?

10. There are nineteen children in the classroom. Sixteen children go out to play. How many children are in the classroom now?

(91) Counting in twos

Learning objective	Resources
Count on or back in ones, twos, fives and tens and use this knowledge to derive the multiples of 2, 5 and 10 to the tenth multiple.	Number snake 0–20 (photocopiable page 94) for each child
Type of starter Recall	

Using the snake, count together in twos from 2 to 20 and back again.

Ask: *What are the numbers called that we have said?* (Even numbers.)
Do you know where to start when you are counting the odd numbers?

Using the snake, count together from 1 to 19 and back again.

Ask: *Are these odd or even numbers?*

1.   2, 4, 6

2.   1, 3, 5

3.   8, 10, 12

4.   7, 9, 11

5.   14, 16, 18, 20

6.   13, 15, 17, 19

Answers

1.   even

2.   odd

3.   even

4.   odd

5.   even

6.   odd

(92) Doubles Snap

Learning objective	Resources
Recall the doubles of all numbers to at least 10	A set of 'Domino doubles' cards (photocopiable page 93); enough sets of numeral cards 0–10 (photocopiable page 88) for each child to have an even number card
Type of starter Recall	

Explain that you are going to show the children a 'Domino double' (such as double 2). The children who have the number that equals the total for this domino (for example, 4) should hold it up and say 'Snap'.

Continue until all the 'Domino doubles' cards have been used at least three times.

No set answers

(93) Halves and quarters

Resources
20 interlocking cubes for each child and a teaching set

Learning objective
Use the vocabulary of halves and quarters in context.

Type of starter
Rehearse

Mental strategies
Children can use their doubles to 10. Remind them that they can use what they know about doubles to find halves. For example, if they know that double 4 is 8 then half of 8 must be 4. They can also use halving and halving again to work mentally to find quarters.

Answers

1. 3
2. 5
3. 4
4. 7
5. 10
6. 9

7. 3
8. 1
9. 5
10. 4

Make a tower of four cubes and say: *Here are four cubes. What is half of four? How can we use these cubes to find the answer?* Demonstrate that the cubes can be broken into two equal towers.

Remind the children of the mental strategies that they can use to find halves, then check with the cubes. Not all children will feel confident to do this yet.

Now ask the children to find the following halves using their cubes.

1. What is half of 6?

2. What is half of 10?

3. What is half of 8?

4. What is half of 14?

5. What is half of 20?

6. What is half of 18?

Now repeat this for quarters. Say: *Look at this tower of eight. How can we find how many quarters there are?* Agree that cube tower can be broken into half then half again.

Remind them of the mental strategy of working out half, then halving that, to find quarters.

Now ask:

7. What is a quarter of 12?

8. What is a quarter of 4?

9. What is a quarter of 20?

10. What is a quarter of 16?

(94) Groups of 2 and 5

Learning objective
Solve practical problems that involve combining groups of 2, 5 or 10, or sharing into equal groups.

Type of starter
Rehearse

Mental strategies
Ask the children to explain how they calculated the answers. Some may count in twos, keeping a tally with their fingers of how many twos they have counted. This strategy can also be used for counting in fives.

Resources
A number line 0–30 for each child

Explain that you will ask some questions about combining groups of two. Remind the children that if they are unsure of the answer they can count on in twos on the number line. Say:

1. What is 2 and 2?

2. What is three groups of 2?

3. Count eight hops of 2 on the number line. What is the answer?

4. Count ten hops of 2. What is that?

5. What is four groups of 2?

Now explain to the children that you will ask them to combine groups of 5. Remind them that they can use their number line to count on in fives if they need help. Say:

6. What is two groups of 5?

7. What is three groups of 5?

8. What is four groups of 5?

9. What is five groups of 5?

10. What is six groups of 5?

Answers
1. 4
2. 6
3. 16
4. 20
5. 8

6. 10
7. 15
8. 20
9. 25
10. 30

BLOCK E

(95) Count in ones and tens

Resources	Learning objective
A board or flipchart	Count on or back in ones, twos, fives and tens and use this knowledge to derive the multiples of 2, 5 and 10 to the tenth multiple.
	Type of starter
	Recall

No set answers

Draw a blank number line 0–10. Ask volunteers to write the following numbers under the line:

1. 6
2. 2
3. 9
4. 3

5. 7
6. 1
7. 5
8. 8

Ask: *Which number is missing?* (4)

Draw a blank number line 0–100. Ask volunteers to write these numbers:

9. 40
10. 80
11. 10
12. 30

13. 70
14. 50
15. 20
16. 60

Ask: *Which number is missing?* (90)

(96) Count in tens

Resources	Learning objective
A board or flipchart	Count on or back in ones, twos, fives and tens and use this knowledge to derive the multiples of 2, 5 and 10 to the tenth multiple.
	Type of starter
	Recall

No set answers

Draw a number line 0–100. Count together in tens from 0 to 100 and back, pointing to each line in turn.

Ask individuals to point to the correct line when you say a number.

1. 20
2. 50
3. 90
4. 60
5. 10

6. 70
7. 40
8. 80
9. 30

Repeat until each child has had a turn.

⑼⁷ **Doubles**

Learning objective Recall the doubles of all numbers to at least 10. **Type of starter** Recall **Mental strategies** Children can double any number to ten by counting on, keeping a tally with their fingers. They should only use this strategy if they do not 'know' the answer.	**Resources** None

Explain to the children that you will ask for double numbers to ten, such as: *What is double 2?* Ask the children to work mentally to find the answer if they do not know it. Say:

1. What is double 2?

2. How much is double 5?

3. What is double 10?

4. What is double 4?

5. How much is double 3?

6. What is double 7?

7. What is double 8?

8. What is double 6?

9. How much is double 9?

10. How much is double 1?

Answers

1.   4
2.   10
3.   20
4.   8
5.   6
6.   14
7.   16
8.   12
9.   18
10. 2

BLOCK E

(98) **Count in twos and fives**

Resources	**Learning objectives**
Number snake 0–20 (photocopiable page 94) for each child	Count on or back in ones, twos, fives and tens and use this knowledge to derive the multiples of 2, 5 and 10 to the tenth multiple.
	Type of starter Recall

No set answers	Count together in twos from 0 to 20 and back again. Ask: *Have we counted the even numbers or the odd numbers?*
	Count together in twos from 1 to 19 and back again. Ask: *Have we counted the odd numbers or the even numbers?*
	Ask the children how they remember which numbers are odd and even. Collect several answers.
	Count together in fives:
	1. from 0 to 20 and back again
	2. from 5 to 20, then back to 0
	3. from 10 to 20, then back to 0.

(99) **Quarters**

Resources	**Learning objective**
24 cubes for each child	Use the vocabulary of halves and quarters in context.
	Type of starter Rehearse
	Mental strategies Children can halve then halve again. If necessary, demonstrate this technique using cubes.

Answers	Ask the children to work mentally where they can. They can use their cubes if they need help. Explain that you would like them to find the answers to these 'find a quarter' questions.
1. 2	
2. 4	1. What is a quarter of 8?
3. 3	
4. 5	2. What is a quarter of 16?
5. 6	
	3. Jill has 12 sweets. She shares them into quarters. How many sweets are there in each pile?
	4. Paul has 20 football cards. He shares these into quarters. How many cards are there in each pile?
	5. There are 24 grapes on the plate. These are shared into quarters. How many are there in each pile?

(100) Combining groups of 2

Learning objective
Solve practical problems that involve combining groups of 2, 5 or 10, or sharing into equal groups.

Type of starter
Refine

Mental strategies
Children can count on in twos, keeping a tally on their fingers if necessary of how many twos they need. So, for six twos, they can count 2, 4, 6, 8, 10, 12. Suggest that they try this then check the answer with cubes.

Resources
20 interlocking cubes for each child

Explain to the children that you would like them to count out groups of 2. Say: *Count out two separate groups of 2. Now combine them. How many cubes do you have altogether? So 2 and 2 makes 4.*

When the children are clear about what to do, say:

1. Make three groups of 2. How many is that altogether?

2. Make five groups of 2. How many is that altogether?

3. Make four groups of 2. How many is that altogether?

4. Make six groups of 2. How many is that altogether?

5 Make eight groups of 2. How many is that altogether?

6. Make seven groups of 2. How many is that altogether?

7. Make nine groups of 2. How many is that altogether?

8. Make ten groups of 2. How many is that altogether?

Answers
1. 6
2. 10
3. 8
4. 12
5. 16
6. 14
7. 18
8. 20

BLOCK E

(101) **Groups of 5 and 10**

Resources
50 counters or cubes for each pair

Learning objective
Solve practical problems that involve combining groups of 2, 5 or 10, or sharing into equal groups.

Type of starter
Refine

Mental strategies
Children can use their groups of counters to count up in fives or tens. Some may manage to count up without the aid of the counters, but may like to keep a tally of the count.

Answers

1. 15
2. 20
3. 30
4. 35
5. 25

6. 20
7. 40
8. 50
9. 30

Organise the children to work in pairs. Ask them to count their counters or cubes into groups of 5 and place them in groups in front of them.

Now say: *Choose two of your groups. Count in fives: 5, 10, 15. So three groups of 5 is 15. Now try these:*

1. What is three groups of 5?

2. What is four groups of 5?

3. What is six groups of 5?

4. What is seven groups of 5?

5. What is five groups of 5?

Now ask the children to place their counters or cubes into groups of 10. Remind them, if necessary, that they can combine two groups of 5 to make 10. Say:

6. What is two groups of 10?

7. How much is four groups of 10?

8. What is five groups of 10?

9. How much is three groups of 10?

(102) Groups of 2, 5 and 10

Learning objective Solve practical problems that involve combining groups of 2, 5 or 10, or sharing into equal groups. **Type of starter** Rehearse **Mental strategies** Check that the children are making equal groups and that they can say the sentence: 'a shared into equal groups of b is c.'	**Resources** 30 cubes for each child

Ask the children to count out ten of their cubes. Now ask them to put these into two equal groups.

Ask: *How many cubes are there in each group? So 10 shared into two equal groups is 5.* Now say:

1. Count out 15 cubes. Put these into equal groups of 5. How many groups are there?

2. Count out 20 cubes. Put these into equal groups of 10. How many groups are there?

3. Count out 6 cubes. Put these into equal groups of 2. How many groups are there?

4. Count out 20 cubes. Put these into equal groups of 5. How many groups are there?

5. Count out 30 cubes. Put these into equal groups of 10. How many groups are there?

Answers

1. 3
2. 2
3. 3
4. 4
5. 3

Numeral cards 0-10

0	1	2
3	4	5
6	7	8
9	10	=

Numeral cards 11–20

11	12	13
14	15	16
17	18	19
20	+	−

Number tracks 1–10

| 1 | 2 | 3 | 4 | 5 | 6 | 7 | 8 | 9 | 10 |

| 1 | 2 | 3 | 4 | 5 | 6 | 7 | 8 | 9 | 10 |

| 1 | 2 | 3 | 4 | 5 | 6 | 7 | 8 | 9 | 10 |

| 1 | 2 | 3 | 4 | 5 | 6 | 7 | 8 | 9 | 10 |

Fact cards: subtraction

5 – 0	4 – 4
5 – 1	3 – 0
5 – 2	3 – 1
5 – 3	3 – 2
5 – 4	3 – 3
5 – 5	2 – 0
4 – 0	2 – 1
4 – 1	2 – 2
4 – 2	1 – 0
4 – 3	1 – 1

Tens number lines 0-100

0	10	20	30	40	50	60	70	80	90	100

0	10	20	30	40	50	60	70	80	90	100

0	10	20	30	40	50	60	70	80	90	100

0	10	20	30	40	50	60	70	80	90	100

Domino doubles

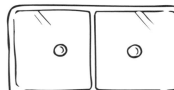
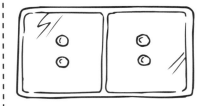

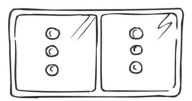
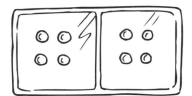
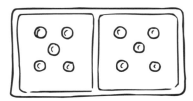

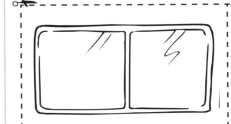
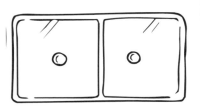
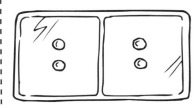

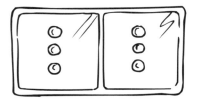
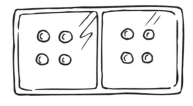
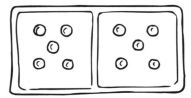

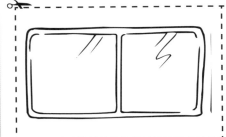
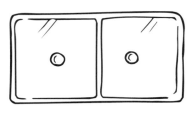
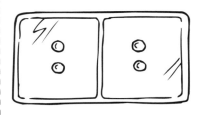

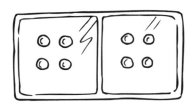
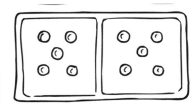

Number snake 0-20

Make 10 cards

■ Enlarge this page to A3 and cut it in half to make two A4 sheets. Enlarge each A4 sheet onto A3 card. Cut out each fact card.

□ + 0 = 10	0 + □ = 10
□ + 1 = 10	1 + □ = 10
□ + 2 = 10	2 + □ = 10
□ + 3 = 10	3 + □ = 10
□ + 4 = 10	4 + □ = 10
□ + 5 = 10	5 + □ = 10
□ + 6 = 10	6 + □ = 10
□ + 7 = 10	7 + □ = 10
□ + 8 = 10	8 + □ = 10
□ + 9 = 10	9 + □ = 10
□ + 10 = 10	10 + □ = 10

Level 1: Oral and mental assessments

Teachers' notes

Time: 20 minutes for each complete paper.

- Children should sit so that they are unable to see each other's work.
- Do not explain questions or read numbers to the children.
- The test may be administered to groups of children or to the whole class.
- There are 20 marks available for each paper.
- The tests consist of ten oral questions and five practical and oral assessments.
- The oral questions could be administered to a class or to smaller groups, if desired.
- Less confident learners could give their answers orally to a teaching assistant or other adult who could record their answers.
- The oral and practical assessment questions are to be delivered to a maximum of four children. This will enable the adult delivering the assessment to make a more detailed assessment of a child's proficiency and also make it possible to identify areas for future development.

Delivering the tests
- Read questions no more than twice to the children.
- Allow five seconds for each answer.
- Answers to be recorded on the answer sheets provided.
- One mark per question: 20 marks total.

Say to the children:
'I am going to read some questions for you to answer. I will read each question twice. You will have five seconds to answer each question.'
'For most of the questions you will write your answer in a box.' [Show example]
'For some questions, you may need to tick the right answer.'
'If you make a mistake, you should cross it out and write your answer again clearly.'

Levelling the children
Add together the marks from the oral and mental test and the oral and practical assessment. (Possible total: 20 marks)

Below Level 1	0 – 7 marks
Low Level 1	8 – 12 marks
Secure Level 1	13 – 15 marks
High Level 1	16 – 20 marks

This assessment reflects a child's performance in mental maths. When awarding an end-of-year teacher assessment level, teachers also need to consider a child's performance on periodic and day-to-day assessments across all learning objectives.

Test 1: Mental maths assessment

Part 1: Oral and mental questions

Time: 20 minutes (both parts).

- Read questions no more than twice to the children.
- Allow five seconds for each answer.
- Answers to be recorded on the answer sheet on page 98.
- One mark per question: 10 marks total.

Resources

A cone; three identical, transparent containers (labelled A, B, C), filled to different capacities, with only B being exactly half full; one large square.

	Question	Answer
1	What number is 1 more than 12?	13
2	Write the number which is the same as one ten and five units.	15
3	Find the difference between 9 and 6.	3
4	*(Hold up a cone.)* What is the name of this shape? Tick the right answer.	cone
5	I have 6p. If I save 10p this week how much will I have?	16p
6	*(Show containers.)* Which of these containers is half full?	B
7	What is the third month of the year? Tick the right answer.	March
8	Find the total of 6 and 4.	10
9	Listen to these numbers: 17, 16, 15.... What is the next number in this sequence?	14
10	*(Imitate folding the square diagonally.)* If I fold this square like this, what shape will I make? Tick the right answer.	triangle

End of test

Name   Date

Test 1: Mental maths assessment

Part 1: Oral and mental assessment answer sheet

	Answer	Mark
1		
2		
3		
4	cube ☐ cone ☐ sphere ☐	
5		
6		
7	February ☐ March ☐ April ☐	
8		
9		
10	square ☐ rectangle ☐ triangle ☐	

End of test   **Total** | |

Test 1: Mental maths assessment

Part 2: Oral and practical assessment

- Instructions and answers to be given orally to groups of no more than four children.
- Two marks per question: 10 marks total.

Resources

Multilink cubes; balance scales; selection of small classroom objects of different mass (eg rubber, pencil, toy car, scissors); two sets of numeral cards 1–9; colour labels: red, yellow, blue, green; 5p, 10p, 20p, 2p coins and 20 x 1p coins.

	Question	Mark
11	Use cubes. Ask each child, in turn, to count out a number of cubes (between 12-16). Ask the child to write down the number of cubes.	1 mark
	Rearrange the cubes. Ask the child how many cubes there are now. Then ask the child how many cubes there would be if you added/took away a cube.	1 mark
12	Use balance scales, classroom objects and cubes. As a group, ask the children to work together to order the objects in order of mass, with the lightest first.	1 mark
	Next, ask the first child to choose an object and estimate its mass in cubes. Finally, ask the child to check their estimate. Repeat with the other children. *(Assessment is about child's ability to estimate and use equipment to check estimates.)*	1 mark
13	Use colour labels and one set of numeral cards. Lay each of the colour labels in a horizontal line across the table. Put the numbers going vertically up the left hand side, to create a simple axis for a pictogram. Tell the children you have collected data about favourite colours and they need to complete the pictogram. Ask each child, in turn, to use cubes to complete their part of the pictogram. Child A: red was the favourite colour of 6 children; Child B: yellow = 3; Child C: blue = 9; Child D: green = 7.	1 mark
	Ask each child a question: A: What was the difference between the number of children liking the two least popular colours? (3) B: How many children liked blue and yellow altogether? (12) C: How many fewer children liked red than green? (1) D: What was the total number of children who liked the most popular colours? (16)	1 mark
14	Use two sets of numeral cards 1–9. Place each set on the table, face down. Ask each child, in turn, to take two cards. Ask them to add them together. Next, ask them to make a subtraction from the two cards.	1 mark
	Then, ask them to add/subtract 10 to or from their number.	1 mark
15	Use coins (as above). Lay them all on the table. Ask each child to find: Child A: 5p; Child B: 20p; Child C: 2p; Child D: 10p.	1 mark
	Ask each child to match their coin with the correct number of 1p coins.	1 mark
End of test	**Total**	10 marks

Test 1: Mental maths assessment

Part 2: Oral and practical teacher's observation sheet

- This space can be used to record teacher's observations of pupil performance and marks gained.
- Make best fit judgements, when awarding marks. There are a total of 10 marks.

Name: _____

Question	Assessment outcome	Mark
11	• Counts and writes numbers up to 20. (1 mark) • Recounts accurately or knows there is still same number. Calculates one more/less. (1 mark)	
12	• Orders objects in order of mass. (1 mark) • Estimates and weighs an object using cubes. (1 mark)	
13	• Uses cubes to complete their part of a pictogram. (1 mark) • Extracts information from the pictogram to answer a question. (1 mark)	
14	• Uses two one-digit numbers to create and calculate an addition and a subtraction sentence. (1 mark) • Adds or subtracts 10 to a one-digit number. (1 mark)	
15	• Correctly identifies single coins up to 20p. (1 mark) • Matches 1p coins to single coins up to 20p. (1 mark)	
End of test	**Total**	

Test 2: Mental maths assessment

Part 1: Oral and mental questions

Time: 20 minutes (both parts).
- Read questions no more than twice to the children.
- Allow five seconds for each answer.
- Answers to be recorded on the answer sheet on page 102.
- One mark per question: 10 marks total.

Resources

Analogue clock (minute hand on 12, hour hand on 4); two large squares (same size).

	Question	Answer
1	Jim has seven balls. He throws one of them to Kim. How many does he have left?	6
2	Write the number seventeen.	17
3	What is double 4?	8
4	I am thinking of a shape. It has three sides and three corners. What is it? Tick the right answer.	triangle
5	How many do I add to 3 to make 10?	7
6	Look at the height of this door. Is it longer or shorter than a metre? Tick the right answer.	longer
7	What day comes after Saturday? Tick the right answer.	Sunday
8	Look at the clock. What time is it?	4 o'clock or 4:00
9	Listen to these numbers: 2, 4, 6, 8,10.... What is the next number in this sequence?	12
10	*(Show squares.)* If I join these two squares together, what shape will I make? Tick the right answer.	rectangle

End of test

Name	Date

Test 2: Mental maths assessment

Part 1: Oral and mental assessment answer sheet

	Answer			Mark
1				
2				
3				
4	triangle ☐	square ☐	circle ☐	
5				
6	longer ☐	shorter ☐		
7	Friday ☐	Monday ☐	Sunday ☐	
8				
9				
10	square ☐	cube ☐	rectangle ☐	
End of test		**Total**		

Test 2: Mental maths assessment

Part 2: Oral and practical assessment

- Instructions and answers to be given orally to groups of no more than four children.
- Two marks per question: 10 marks total.

Resources

Numeral cards: 11, 12, 13, 14; multilink cubes; two dice; £1 coins and pictures of toys each labelled: £6, £7, £8, £9; straws, three for each child, with each one being a different length; 3D shapes: cube, sphere, pyramid, cone and labels "Straight edges" and "Curved edges".

	Question		Mark
11	Use numeral cards and multilink cubes. Give each child a numeral card. Ask each child, in turn to read the number on their card.		1 mark
	Next, ask them to count enough cubes to match the number on their card. Ask how many there would be if there were one more/less.		1 mark
12	Use two dice. For each child, shake both dice and ask the child to make an addition for the two numbers.		1 mark
	Then, ask them to make a subtraction for the two numbers.		1 mark
13	Use the straws. Give each child three straws (as above). In turn, ask each child to show you their longest straw. Then, ask them to show their shortest straw.		1 mark
	Finally, ask them to order their straws from shortest to longest.		1 mark
14	Use £1 coins and toy pictures. Give each child a picture of a toy. In turn, ask them to count out coins to match the price of the picture.		1 mark
	Then, ask each child to work out how much change they would get if they gave the shopkeeper £10.		1 mark
15	Use 3D shapes and labels (as above). Give each child a shape. Ask each child to name their shape.		1 mark
	Place the labels on the table with a space between them. Read the labels to the children. Then, in turn, ask each child to place their shape under the correct label, explaining their choice.		1 mark
End of test		**Total**	10 marks

Test 2: Mental maths assessment

Part 2: Oral and practical teacher's observation sheet

- This space can be used to record teacher's observations of pupil performance and marks gained.
- Make best fit judgements, when awarding marks. There are a total of 10 marks.

Name: _____

Question	Assessment outcome	Mark
11	• Reads numbers up to 20. (1 mark) • Counts cubes to match numbers up to 20. Calculates one more/less. (1 mark)	
12	• Adds two single-digit numbers. (1mark) • Subtracts two single-digit numbers. (1 mark)	
13	• Finds longest and shortest straw out of three straws. (1 mark) • Orders three straws from shortest to longest. (1 mark)	
14	• Uses £1 coins to pay for an object. (1 mark) • Works out change from £10. (1 mark)	
15	• Names a 3D shape. (1 mark) • Sorts 3D shapes according to given criteria. (1 mark)	
End of test	**Total**	

Level 2: Oral and mental assessments

Teachers' notes

Time: 20 minutes for each complete paper.

- Children should sit so that they are unable to see each other's work.
- Do not explain questions or read numbers to the children.
- The test may be administered to groups of children or to the whole class.
- There are 20 marks available for each paper.
- The tests consist of 15 oral questions and 5 practical and oral assessments.
- The oral questions could be administered to a class or to smaller groups, if desired.
- Less confident learners could give their answers orally to a teaching assistant or other adult who could record their answers.
- The oral and practical assessment questions are to be delivered to a maximum of four children. This will enable the adult delivering the assessment to make a more detailed assessment of a child's proficiency and also make it possible to identify areas for future development.

Delivering the tests

- Read questions no more than twice to the children.
- Allow five seconds for each answer.
- Answers to be recorded on the answer sheets provided.
- One mark per question: 20 marks total.

Say to the children:

'I am going to read some questions for you to answer. 'I will read each question twice. You will have five seconds to answer each question.'

'For most of the questions you will write your answer in a box' [Show example]

'For some questions, you may need to tick the right answer.'

'If you make a mistake, you should cross it out and write your answer again clearly.'

Levelling the children

Add together the marks from the oral and mental test and the oral and practical assessment. (Possible total: 20 marks)

Below Level 2	0 – 7 marks
Low Level 2	8 – 12 marks
Secure Level 2	13 – 15 marks
High Level 2	16 – 20 marks

This assessment reflects a child's performance in mental maths. When awarding an end-of-year teacher assessment level, teachers also need to consider a child's performance on periodic and day-to-day assessments across all learning objectives.

Test 1: Mental maths assessment

Part 1: Oral and mental questions

Time: 20 minutes (both parts).

- Read questions no more than twice to the children.
- Allow five seconds for each answer.
- Answers to be recorded on the answer sheet on pages 107–108.
- One mark per question: 15 marks total.

Resources

A ball; three containers (A, B, C) of differing sizes, with only one (A) holding more than a litre.

	Question	Answer
1	What number is 1 more than 124?	125
2	Three hundred and twenty-six – how many tens?	2 tens
3	Find the difference between 43 and 37.	6
4	*(Hold up a ball.)* What is this shape? Tick the correct shape.	sphere
5	I have £1. A comic costs 45p. How much change will I get?	55p
6	*(Use containers.)* Which of these containers would hold more than a litre?	A
7	How many hours are there in one day?	24
8	When I doubled a number the answer was 14. What was the number?	7
9	I need 28 books for Class 2. If a box holds 10 books, how many boxes do I need?	3
10	I am thinking of a shape. It has five straight sides and no right angles. What is it?	pentagon
11	What is 6 x 5?	30
12	I start watching a television programme at 4:45. It finishes half an hour later. What time will it be?	5:15
13	What is ten less than 63?	53
14	I have 8 sweets. I eat one quarter of them. How many have I left?	6
15	4 x 5 = 20. Use these numbers to make a division sentence.	20 ÷ 4 = 5 or 20 ÷ 5 = 4

End of test

PHOTOCOPIABLE **SCHOLASTIC**

Name   Date

Test 1: Mental maths assessment

Part 1: Oral and mental assessment answer sheet (1 of 2)

	Answer	Mark
1		
2		
3		
4	cube ▢ pyramid ▢ sphere ▢	
5		
6		
7		
8		

Name   Date

Mental maths assessment

Part 1: Oral and mental assessment answer sheet (2 of 2)

	Answer	Mark
9		
10		
11		
12		
13		
14		
15	4 x 5 = 20	

End of test   **Total**

Test 1: Mental maths assessment

Part 2: Oral and practical assessment

- Instructions and answers to be given orally to groups of no more than four children.
- One mark per question: five marks total.

Resources

Selection of paper regular 2D shapes, eg squares, rectangles, triangles, circles; numeral cards 50-100; page from a calendar with a one month view; four analogue clocks; water; transparent litre measuring jug.

	Question	Mark
16	Use 2D shapes. Give two different shapes to each child. Ask each child, in turn, to fold one of their shapes in half exactly and to fold the other shape into quarters.	1 mark
17	Use numeral cards. Give each child four cards. Ask each child to order their cards, from smallest to largest. Next, ask each child to read their cards. Finally, for each child, choose a card and ask them to give the next three numbers.	1 mark
18	Use calendar. Place calendar in the middle of the table. Start by asking general questions to introduce the calendar: What month is this? How many days are there in this month? How do you know? Then, in turn, ask: Child A: What day is the 24th? Child B: How many Sundays are there in this month? Child C: What day was the 2nd? Child D: What day would the first day of the next month fall on?	1 mark
19	Use analogue clocks. Ask each child, in turn, to show different times on their clock and then answer a question. Child A: 6:45 - What time will it be in 15 minutes? Child B: 4:15 - What time will it be in half an hour? Child C: 12:30 - What time will it be in 45 minutes? Child D: 4:45 - What time will it be in half an hour?	1 mark
20	Use litre measuring jug and water. Ask each child to fill the jug to different capacities. Child A: 500ml; Child B: 300ml; Child C: 1 litre; Child D: 800ml.	1 mark
End of test	Total	**5 marks**

Test 1: Mental maths assessment

Part 2: Oral and practical teacher's observation sheet

- This space can be used to record teacher's observations of pupil performance and marks gained.
- Make best fit judgements, when awarding marks. There are a total of five marks.

Name: _____

Question	Assessment outcome	Mark
16	• Folds one shape in half. • Folds one shape into quarters. (1 mark)	
17	• Orders four number cards. • Reads four number cards. • Identifies smallest/largest number. • Says next three numbers. (1 mark)	
18	• Extracts information from a calendar. (1 mark)	
19	• Shows the time on an analogue clock to 15 minute intervals. • Works out time intervals. (1 mark)	
20	• Fills a capacity jug to nearest 100ml. (1 mark)	
End of test	**Total**	

Mental maths teacher record sheet

Teacher's name: _____

Name of starter	PNS objectives covered	Block/unit	Date activity was used

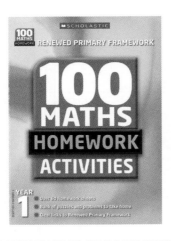
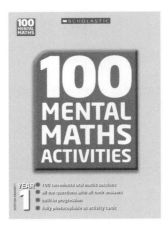